OP 8⁵ᶜ

THE WORLD OF THE BLACK BEAR

LIVING WORLD BOOKS
John K. Terres, Editor

The World of the Beaver by Leonard Lee Rue III
The World of the Black Bear by Joe Van Wormer
The World of the Bobcat by Joe Van Wormer
The World of the Coyote by Joe Van Wormer
The World of the Great Horned Owl by G. Ronald Austing
   and John B. Holt, Jr.
The World of the Porcupine by David F. Costello
The World of the Raccoon by Leonard Lee Rue III
The World of the Red-tailed Hawk by G. Ronald Austing
The World of the White-tailed Deer by Leonard Lee Rue III

THE WORLD OF THE
Black Bear

TEXT AND PHOTOGRAPHS BY

JOE VAN WORMER

J. B. LIPPINCOTT COMPANY

PHILADELPHIA AND NEW YORK

To my Mother and Father, who were the first to show me the wonders of wild life.

Contents

Meet the Black Bear   13

Spring   48

Summer   82

Autumn   102

Winter   124

Conclusion   136

Black Bear Subspecies   152

Bibliography   155

Index   161

Meet the Black Bear

EVERYONE SEEMS TO KNOW a lot about bears. Most children first meet the animal in the form of a stuffed toy, and thousands of youngsters go to bed each night with a worn and often dirty "Teddy" bear. It may only slightly resemble any known bear species either in shape or color, but through constant reminders by adults the child learns it is a "bear." Later, children's fiction, such as the classic "Goldilocks and the Three Bears," adds to the child's misconception of the animal. Television and movies further confuse the issue. Eventually, the youngster will see a real bear—usually at the zoo—but its actions will have been influenced by years of captivity and it will not act much like a bear, or, rather, much like the way a bear acts in the wild.

It is little wonder then that most of us grow up knowing a lot about bears, most of it wrong.

The black bear belongs to the family Ursidae, which has three other North American members: the grizzly bear, the big brown bear, and the polar bear. The grizzly lives in western and northern Canada, Alaska, and a limited area of the Rocky Mountains in the United States. The range of the big brown bear is limited to the southern and southeastern coastal areas of Alaska. Polar bears are found in the circumpolar sea ice areas of the far north.

All these species evolved from a family of small tree-climbing carnivorous mammals called Miacidae that lived fifty million years ago and was also the origin of coyotes, wolves, foxes, and raccoons. Males are called "boars"; females, "sows"; and the young, "cubs."

13

A male American black bear. This is probably an average-sized adult male.

Only a few grizzly bears are left in the United States (exclusive of Alaska), but they share a limited range with black bears in certain sections of the Rocky Mountains.

Meet the Black Bear

The black bear apparently got its name from its color. The first settlers from Europe were acquainted with Old Country bear species and so, of course, this American species was nothing really new. It was a bear and it was black, so it was called a black bear. Eventually this common name was adopted scientifically and American black bear became an official designation.

It is the smallest of all North American bears as well as the most numerous and most widely dispersed. In fact, black bears are and have probably been more numerous than any other kind of bear anywhere in the world.

The big brown bear (Kodiak bear), found only in Alaska, is the world's largest carnivore.

The World of the Black Bear

All bears, including those in Europe and Asia, have a similar and distinctive appearance, and there is little likelihood of confusing them with other animals when they can be clearly seen. The black bear is a large animal with a heavy body that sometimes appears barrellike. Its stout legs seem too short for the size of the animal, and it walks with a flat-footed shuffling gait. It has a long muzzle with a straight facial profile and medium-sized, rounded, erect ears. The fur is shaggy, long, and soft, and practically conceals the very short bobbed tail, which is usually under 6 inches long. The outline of its back is straight.

Color is not a reliable means of identifying black bears for they can

The polar bear inhabits the circumpolar sea-ice areas of the Far North. It eats much more flesh than other North American bear species and probably has the best eyesight of any.

Meet the Black Bear

be various shades from black to white. However, most have a glossy black coat, a brown snout, and an occasional white patch on the chest. Strangely enough, the majority of black bears in the east are black with only an occasional color variation, but as one moves westward more and more browns, blonds, and colors other than black show up. William H. Wright in 1910 described various colors of black bears he had seen in northern Idaho and western Montana as seal-brown, light cream, yellow-brown, jet black, olive-yellow, mouse-colored, and steel-blue. In 1950, two gray-colored black bears were recorded in Colorado. This is the first known evidence of this color phase.

This black bear, like all bears, has a distinctive appearance and is not easily confused with any other animal.

Female black bear with nine-month-old cub that is a gray-brown color.

This large bear, brown color phase, was photographed in the late spring. It is probably a male.

*A large cub in Crater Lake National Park that is a very light brown color—
almost blond.*

White chest patches such as this bear has are found on only a few specimens.

The World of the Black Bear

Although I have kept no accurate account, the areas where I have personally observed many bears, Yellowstone National Park and Crater Lake National Park, have about as many brown color phases of black bears as they have black. A recent study in Saskatchewan indicated that brown color phases predominate in that region. Of a total of eighteen cubs collected there, fourteen were brown. Joseph Grinnell and his associates reported that "In California, bears of the brown color phase seem to be much more numerous than those of the black phase."

The light-brown color phases of the black bear are seldom found in Alaska. Instead there are rich, luxuriant chocolate-brown animals which are frequently mistaken for the big brown or grizzly bear. Even more unique is the blue-gray or glacial phase, which is quite rare and is generally confined in its distribution to the Alaskan coastal areas lying between Cross Sound and Cape St. Elias in the Gulf of Alaska.

One bear of this coloration, however, was captured in New York in 1946. This animal was a female cub of a light bluish-gray color with tan muzzle and ears. She had two black litter mates. At the time this specimen died at about 1½ years of age, her coat had changed to chocolate brown. This color change does not seem to be experienced by the true "glacier" bear.

Quite likely the most unusual of all black bear color phases, because it is about as far removed from black as you can get, is the Kermode subspecies. Arthur C. Popham, Jr., who was permitted to take one of these carefully protected bears for a zoological specimen, describes the pelt as "snowy white, the nose a grayish beige, and the eyes brown. The pads of the feet were reddish brown." Alan Best, Curator of the Vancouver, British Columbia, Zoo, in describing a Kermode on exhibition there, mentioned its "almost pink colouring."

This subspecies was unknown until 1900, when Dr. William T. Hornaday, New York Zoological Park director, was shown an unusual, pure-white bearskin. When its origin was traced to British Columbia,

20

Dr. Hornaday enlisted the aid of Francis Kermode, then curator of the British Columbia Provincial Museum at Victoria, B.C. In 1905, Dr. Hornaday announced the discovery of a new and very rare black bear. It was named for Kermode.

Black bears generally remain the same color all their adult lives, although a case was reported of a cinnamon-colored bear which molted into a black phase after two years in captivity. However, there are usually some slight color variations due to the season, the age of the animal's coat, and the weathering it has undergone.

There seems to be no predictable pattern of these color phases. Black females have both brown and black cubs, and so do brown females. It is not uncommon to see a female with twins or triplets of different colors. They may be black as well as any of many different shades of brown, from blond to chocolate.

Because of these different color phases, a great many people still believe that there are separate species of brown and cinnamon bears in the United States. I have recently been involved in rather heated arguments with outdoorsmen who should know better but refuse to accept any proof that there is no separate species of cinnamon bear.

In Bend, Oregon, where I live, the local high school athletic teams are known as "Lava Bears." This name originated, I am told, many years ago when a noted humorist visiting the area wrote a piece for his syndicated newspaper column about the "lava bears" that inhabited the lava flows and volcanic cones in central Oregon. This "lava bear" may have been based upon local stories, or the humorist's imagination, or the fact that some brown-phase black bear had been seen in the flows of black lava that are found in the pine forests near Bend. Regardless of the origin of the story, the humorist did such a good job of it that there are some in the area who still believe that a separate species of small brown "lava bears" still lives in these barren fields of jumbled volcanic spewings.

A black bear continues to grow until it is four or five years old.

21

The World of the Black Bear

However, there is considerable variation in size and weight between individuals, between males and females, between mature animals in different parts of the country, and between spring and fall weights of the same animal. There often seems to be a great deal of confusion about the weight and size of bears killed by hunters. Most weigh about 50 per cent of the estimate when exposed to accurate scales. In the past there have been claims of black bears weighing in excess of 900 pounds, but these apparently were not authenticated. Live weights of animals taken by hunters are generally estimated by taking the weight of a field dressed animal and adding a percentage to make up for the removed portions of the bear. Bears taken in the last ten years whose weight was estimated in approximately this manner included some of the largest specimens on record with weights of 645 pounds, 700 pounds, 720 pounds, and 656 pounds.

Skull measurements are also used as size indications. One of the largest on record is in the University of Florida mammal collection and came from a male bear trapped in Duval County in northeastern Florida. The skull has an over-all length of 13.75 inches and a width of 8.20 inches. The bear weighed 580 pounds, although at the time of weighing he had not eaten for seven days. His normal live weight would have probably been in excess of 600 pounds.

The largest black bear included in the 1964 edition of *Records of North American Big Game*, which is compiled by the Boone and Crockett Club and which is limited to animals taken by hunters, had skull measurements of 13-3/16 inches in length and 8-12/16 inches in width. The estimated weight of this bear was 700 pounds. The second largest black bear included in this record had skull measurements of 13-5/16 inches in length and 8-6/16 inches in width.

While these giant black bears do exist, most individuals will run much smaller. It would be next to impossible to arrive at an "average-size" bear. Females are usually much smaller than males. Adults will generally weigh from 200 to 400 pounds. They will be from 50 to 65

The straight profile of the black bear as compared with the more "dish-faced" look of the grizzly helps distinguish the two species.

inches in length though some have been measured to 72 inches. Shoulder height varies from 27 to 36 inches, but some authorities contend that this is deceiving, as the middle of the back, rather than the shoulder, is the highest part of the body.

In the United States, other than Alaska, there is little chance of confusing the American black bear with any other bear, simply because there are no others—except in a section of the northern and central Rocky Mountains. In this small area black bear and grizzly bear share a common range, and it would be possible to confuse a brown-phase black bear with a grizzly. The grizzly ranges from yellowish to dark brown, nearly black, and usually has white-tipped hairs on its back to give it a grizzled appearance. Consequently, a *black*-colored bear would never be a grizzly.

There are other differences, fortunately. The grizzly is a larger animal than the black bear, but size can be deceiving—a large or mature black bear would be larger than or as large as a small or immature grizzly. The black bear has a straight facial profile while that of the grizzly is concave. The grizzly bear also has a decided shoulder hump; the black bear does not. The foreclaws of a grizzly are longer and straighter than those of the black bear. When tracks are visible and size alone is insufficient for identification, the front-foot imprint of a grizzly has distinct claw marks, whereas that of a black bear shows only toe marks.

There seems to be no way to measure the strength of a black bear, but it has been said that no animal of equal size is more powerful. I, for one, would not argue with this statement. Often a black bear looks slow and sleepy, and its demonstrations of strength appear so easy that they are deceiving. A hungry bear searching for insects or small rodents under old logs and boulders flips them over effortlessly. We constantly hear stories of bears breaking into supposedly well-built cabins for food or wrecking strong wooden commissary boxes left out by careless campers. On those rare occasions when a black bear devel-

24

ops a taste for fresh beef, it generally breaks the animal's neck with one or more powerful blows of the forepaw.

Despite its size and great strength, the black bear is one of our shyest wild animals. It runs first and finds out later what it is running from. Several years ago I was fishing in the Mink Lake Basin of the central Oregon Cascades. This is good bear country, covered with fir and other evergreens. There are many lakes scattered thoughout the area as well as lush mountain meadows and berry patches. It is eight miles or so from the nearest road. Fishing was poor so I gave up and headed back to camp. I noticed a faint wisp of dust hanging in the air above the trail. I looked around quickly and a hundred yards away saw a large black bear going up the hillside through thick waist-high manzanita, moving at top speed like an overgrown jack rabbit.

The slight breeze that just barely ruffled the evergreens was blowing from me toward the bear. The instant it got a whiff of man-tainted air it had started running without waiting to see who I was or if I were dangerous. The chances are that it didn't stop until it had gone a mile or so.

This wariness of potential danger is only one manifestation of the intelligence attributed to the black bear by most students of the animal. In places where man is not a danger but a provider, such as in our national parks, the bear learns quickly that he is not dangerous and is a source of food. Thus we have panhandler bears. Some even develop special tricks to draw more appreciative audiences. Somehow or other these wild bears determine that certain antics, such as sitting up or holding out a paw, bring bigger rewards. Captive bears learn the same thing. These are not stunts taught them by people but tricks they have apparently figured out for themselves.

Another indication of intelligence that I have observed in Yellowstone National Park bears is their ability to associate the sound of garbage trucks and garbage cans with food. They can also recognize the uniform of the park rangers and the vehicles they drive. I once

Black bears in our national parks soon learn the art of begging from passing motorists. Despite constant warnings of the dangers involved, tourists persist in feeding these animals.

watched a bear begging along a Yellowstone road, successfully getting food contributions from passing tourists. A ranger came along, stopped, and got out of his car. The instant the bear saw him it quickly abandoned its begging activities and retreated into the woods.

In most national parks with sizable black bear populations, park engineers have been trying for years to devise a bearproof garbage can. I have no idea how many designs have been tried and found inadequate. The latest model I saw, in 1964, looked as if it might do the job. But bears are quite resourceful and continually do new things in a new way. About the time one thinks one has outsmarted them, they come up with something different.

Black bears have been described as unpredictable individualists that have humor, imagination, respect, and dignity, and are both unpredictable and impulsive. They have also been called treacherous, though I would prefer to think of them as being inconsistent.

Animals in captivity often get such labels because someone forgets that they are still wild even though they may have lost their fear of man. Normally docile captive buck deer have been known to kill people during the rutting season. This was not because they were treacherous but because during this period deer have no friends and abide by no rules. For somewhat this same reason, a pet bear can be dangerous. It is no longer afraid of people, so if it is teased or something unexpected happens, it may slap the very person who thinks the pet is tame. A slap from an animal strong enough to break the neck of a cow with one blow can be, and usually is, disastrous.

Despite the bear's high degree of intelligence, it falls easy prey to a steel trap. Just why seems to be one of nature's mysteries. It may be because the bear really has only one enemy of any significance over most of its range, and that is man. Over the years danger becomes associated with man scent. Consequently, a well-set trap with all remnants of human odor camouflaged with the strong smell of a carrion bait holds no fears for a bear.

Black bear country, the Cascade Mountains of central Oregon.

Meet the Black Bear

The black bear has always inhabited an enormous range, possibly greater than any other North American mammal. It is not too concerned with either temperature or humidity if it has the food and cover it needs. Its territory extends all the way from sea level up through the coniferous forest zone in mountainous areas. However, some observations have indicated that the black bear does not like high altitudes and seldom stays long in areas above 7,000 feet.

The rugged northeastern corner of Oregon is also good bear country.

The World of the Black Bear

The black bear is first and foremost a forest species, but it seems to have a decided preference for open forests. Dense thickets of timber provide the cover, while intermittent semi-open areas of fruit-bearing shrubs, lush grasses, and succulent forbs provide much of the black bear's food.

The black bear's ability to stand erect on its hind feet give it a human appearance which has aroused interest in the species both at present and in the past.

Meet the Black Bear

Ideally, black bear range would be a mixed stand of conifers and hardwoods to provide cover on a year-round basis—a necessity because timidity makes the black bear uncomfortable in large open areas. Streams, ponds, and lakes are also desirable to provide wallows, fish, and drink, along with the necessary moisture for a good growth of trees and berry bushes.

Black bears have a way of getting into positions that are amusing. Much of this is due to their human appearance and actions.

The World of the Black Bear

Before the white man came to North America, black bears could be found in all forested areas. While this is still true generally, the animal's range has been substantially reduced because much forest-covered acreage has been converted to farm lands or cleared for other uses. Consequently, the black bear's present range is in the mountainous sections of Mexico, the western United States, Canada, and Alaska; the mountains of New York, Pennsylvania, and the southern Atlantic States; and the wild forested sections of the Gulf States, the northern part of the Lake States, western Ontario, and the northeastern United States and Canada.

One thing that seems to have created a special feeling for the black bear is the animal's ability to stand on its hind legs. Normally this two-legged stance is taken to give the animal a better view, to check the wind, or to wrestle with an opponent. Though it may occasionally walk a step or two in an erect position, its usual method of movement is on all fours.

One of the first things a young black bear learns is to climb trees. That is its principal means of defense. Grizzly cubs are also good climbers, but mature grizzlies lose this ability. However, this seems to be of little consequence, since a mature grizzly has nothing to fear from any animal in North America, other than man, and there is no food for it to find in trees. Black bears are able to climb trees throughout their lives, though they apparently do very little of it after maturity. A black bear's claws are short and strongly curved. With their aid it can climb anything from small saplings that will hardly hold its weight to giant trees so big that the bear must cling to the trunk like a squirrel.

Climbing is done with the hind feet. The front feet merely hold the animal in place while the bear brings its hind legs forward under its belly. Then the hind legs are extended like pistons, and the bear reaches up for another hold with its front paws. If not in a hurry, the bear will spiral around the tree as it moves upward. Bears tend to climb trees on the uphill side, or the concave side if the tree is bent.

32

One of the first things a black bear cub learns is to climb a tree. They soon become good at it. Climbing is done with the hind feet. While holding on with its front feet, the bear brings its hind legs up, digs into the bark with the claws of its hind feet, and then thrusts upward to grab the trunk with its front feet.

Mature black bears do not lose their ability to climb, but they do less climbing than younger bears.

A yearling black bear takes refuge in a tree to escape a threatening older bear.

However, if a bear is badly frightened and in a hurry, it is a spectacular sight as it goes straight up a tree trunk in great leaps.

Several years ago while driving through Yellowstone in early October I surprised a mature black bear lying a bit too close to the road. It must have expected the car to hit it, and from its prone position made a fantastic leap to the trunk of a tree at the side of the road about 5 feet above ground and stuck there like a bur. Another couple of leaps put it 20 feet up into the tree. It was a revelation to me of both the animal's speed and agility as well as its tree-climbing ability. Bears can climb a tree about as fast as a man can run the same distance on the ground. One observer, who watched a black bear make a rapid ascent up a fir tree, said that he did not believe a pine squirrel could have equaled its speed.

A black bear is not nearly as skillful coming down as it is going up. It backs down the tree in what seems to be a controlled fall, with its claws raking the bark just enough to keep it from falling too fast. The bear usually lets loose a few feet above the ground and lands awkwardly on its haunches.

Cubs, yearlings, and two-year-olds climb a great deal—far more than adult bears. Some of this is just for fun or practice. I watched a yearling chase a Douglas squirrel, *Tamiasciurus douglasii,* up a 6-inch tree in Crater Lake National Park. I do not think the young bear ever really thought it would catch the squirrel, but it just wanted to climb and the squirrel gave it an excuse. The squirrel went to the topmost branches with the young bear right behind. When the bear was practically within reaching distance, the saucy squirrel gave a flirt of its tail and ran right down and over the bear's face and belly to safety. A few minutes later the young bear came sliding down the tree seemingly well-satisfied with its exploit.

It is just as well that these young bears are agile, quick climbers because most adult bears are their potential enemies, especially females with cubs and grouchy old males.

35

The World of the Black Bear

I once spent several days watching bears coming into a remote refuse pit in Crater Lake National Park. I was unable to be sure of just how many individual animals were using this refuse pit because many of them were so similar in appearance I could not be sure of whether I was seeing new ones coming in or previous visitors returning. I guessed that during the period I had seen at least twenty bears. Once there were a dozen scattered about the area that I could see simultaneously. It was apparent that some order of dominance existed, but I was unable to work it out completely. It seemed, in general, that other bears stayed at a safe distance if an old boar or a sow with cubs had

Although their eyesight is poor, black bears have keen hearing and a superb sense of smell. This animal was alert to the approach of another, larger bear, while it was still some distance away.

arrived first. Younger males and females were next in line, while unattached yearlings and two-year-olds came in last. Occasionally, some relationship that I didn't understand permitted several bears to feed at the same time where, normally, it seemed to me, this would have led to a fight or at least to a bluffing contest.

I never did see a female with cubs attempt to route a big male from his feeding, nor did I ever see a big male attempt to scare off a female with cubs.

During the several days I spent observing bears around this refuse pit, I was continually amazed at their ability to detect other bears

This big black male checks the wind for approaching danger.

approaching long before anything was visible. It seemed to me that the bears at the pit could also determine if the approaching animal was dangerous while the newcomer was still at long range.

Black bears have very poor vision. When they stand erect on their hind legs, it is quite often to get a better look at something that to them is probably only a blur. But they more than make up for their lack of keen eyesight by their acute hearing and marvelous sense of smell. The bear's poor eyesight is undoubtedly the principal reason for the occasional surprise meetings in the woods between people and bears. However, anyone who might be concerned about the possibility of such a chance meeting need only do his woods walking with the wind blowing against his back. Any bear in his path will get the wind-driven scent of man and silently vanish into the thickets.

A successful hunter of bears in the early 1900's reported that a captive black bear cub kept at their hunting camp made a perfect watchman. "Nothing ever succeeded in approaching our camp without his knowing it; and this not only before we could hear a sound ourselves, but before we could have expected even his sharp ears or sensitive nostrils to detect anything."

Practically everyone who has ever seen a bear has some kind of story to tell about it. Hunters have always seemed to have had an unusual number of adventures and misadventures with this animal. In recent years these stories mostly involve tales of long chases or the fighting ability of bears or, when some hunter does something foolish and gets into trouble with a wounded bear, a story of the damage it can do to a man. Actually, a black bear stands little chance against modern weapons.

This was not so true some years ago when Indians attacked them with arrows and spears and white pioneers relied on their one-shot muzzle-loaders, with knives and axes as reserve weapons. Bear meat, bear fat, and bearskins were important items to a pioneer or Indian living off the country. They did not kill a bear for sport. It was always

38

Along with its ability to stand erect on its hind feet, the black bear also assumes many poses and positions which have a humanlike quality about them. At least there is sufficient resemblance to add to the bear's reputation as something of a clown.

a necessity, and they occasionally had to take chances which led to wild experiences and narrow escapes, and sometimes no escape at all.

I am inclined to think that because of the bear's resemblance to man, and especially because of its ability and tendency to stand erect on its hind legs, the things it does are more noticeable and more memorable than those of any other animal.

Most of the bear episodes we hear about involve, in some way or another, the black bear's continuous search for food. L. C. Abbie, who has worked for the National Park Service in Yellowstone for about thirty years, has not only seen and heard of a great many black bear adventures but has also been involved in his share of them. During his early years in Yellowstone he and his wife spent a part of each year in a tent house. Mrs. Abbie frequently found it necessary to chase bears out of her kitchen, and their tent had been ripped open and resewn so often that it was just a mass of "scars."

Some years ago, after they had been provided with a house, Mr. Abbie came home from work one day and called to his wife as he walked toward the door. He had been aware of movement within the darker interior of the house and naturally assumed it was his wife. Unknown to him she had gone out on an errand and had left the doors open. As Mr. Abbie went into the house, a large black bear walked calmly out of the living room and faced him. On the floor was the wrapper of a package of cheese it had just eaten, but it had not gotten to the meat and vegetables Mrs. Abbie had out on a counter in preparation for the evening meal. Abbie yelled at the bear, which left in haste but "managed to retain some semblance of dignity."

Mr. Abbie also described to me the various activities of a pair of cubs in the Lake section of the park that kept the whole settlement of park employees amused one summer. One story concerned an evening just at dusk when Abbie was at home reading the newspaper. He heard a gentle pat-pat on the window and looked up to see one of the pair standing on its hind legs looking in through the glass and patting it

40

gently with a forepaw to attract attention. The cub had an expectant look on its face like a child at Christmas. Abbie did not feed the youngster, of course, but was intrigued by the animal's approach to the problem.

One of the stories going around the last time I was in Yellowstone was about a tourist in a small bus-type foreign car, who had stopped to watch a female and two cubs by the side of the road. The female and one of the cubs stood up beside the car on the driver's side while he slipped a couple of crackers out through the window he had opened a crack. In the meantime, the other cub had managed to climb up the side of the vehicle and crawl in through a back window, which the occupants apparently had forgotten was open. Unaware of their uninvited passenger, the tourists decided they'd had enough and drove off. A couple of miles down the road, the driver felt something breathing down his neck and turned around to look squarely into the furry brown face of the cub. Fortunately, they were on a level stretch of road with no deep ditches on either side or they might have had a bad accident. The driver skidded the bus to a screeching halt, and he and his wife jumped out. They lured the cub out of the car with a handful of crackers and went on their way.

A bear's curiosity and stomach always seem to be getting it into trouble.

I saw a big brown male bear in Crater Lake National Park with a hairless spot on his right hip that was about 18 inches long and at least 6 inches wide. One of the park rangers told me that the bear had gotten greedy at a refuse pit the year before and had been badly burned. It is standard practice in this park to set fire to the refuse each day. This old bear had been so intent on the refuse, he forgot to watch the fire.

This seemed a little far-fetched to me, considering the fear most animals have of fire. However, I changed my mind about it after seeing a big black male standing on the smoldering dump searching for food.

41

The World of the Black Bear

The smoke was so thick that at times it completely hid the bear. Every few minutes flames flared up, when this happened the bear would move a few inches and if the smoke got too thick he would stand up for a breath of fresh air. After fifteen minutes or so the animal moved away from the pit and crouched in the shade of a nearby fir tree. He had either satisfied his appetite for the moment or had had enough of the fire and smoke. Along one entire side of the bear the fur was deeply singed.

By the time the first white men in this country got around to creating their own legends about bears, the Indians already had a great stock of stories, and Mr. Bear played an important role in their ceremonies and dances. The Indians were greatly aware of the bear's resemblance to man (which is even more pronounced when the shaggy skin is removed), and it was likely that this resemblance prompted them to assign a special place for the bear in the Happy Hunting Grounds. Also, the Indians' inclination toward a belief in reincarnation as an animal gave both the grizzly and black bear ancestral relationship among them. Many tribes had their bear clans, and to many of these the black bear was known as "Little Brother." Other Indians referred to the bear as "Grandfather." During the early explorations of the present state of Maine, Indians referred to bear signs seen in the woods as "our cousins' tracks."

Different Indian tribes had their own peculiar beliefs in the powers of the bear spirit which, in some instances, assumed a position of great importance in the Indian religion. Both the grizzly and the black bear were honored with this veneration, but the larger, stronger, and more aggressive grizzly was usually accorded a somewhat higher position.

Most of the tribes had great respect for the bear and though they occasionally killed one for food or its warm hide, it was treated with much greater consideration than other animals, such as the deer. Its speedy acceptance into the Happy Hunting Grounds was assured by prayerful chants and appropriate offerings. Not all tribes would kill

42

The tremendous scar on this bear's hip came from a severe burn received when the animal was careless around a refuse pit fire.

The deeply singed area on this animal's left side also was the result of feeding too close to the flames in a burning refuse pit.

bears, however; some feared they might be slaying a reincarnated brother.

The Chippewa considered the bear as something of an expert on herbs because of its claws, which are so well adapted for digging roots. Should a member of the tribe be fortunate enough to dream of a bear during one of their fasting periods, he would become an authority on the use of herbs for curing sickness.

The bear was frequently considered a symbol of courage, strength, and good judgment. To the Pueblo the bear was the symbol of war and medicine, and to the Osage it was a symbol of life or of old age and longevity. The Senecas thought the bones of bears were medicine that would bestow magical powers. On the other hand, the Chiricahua Apache would not eat bear meat or touch it or use the hide for fear of being inflicted with mysterious ills.

In the religion of some tribes the bear was a powerful patron, capable of great curing powers. Tribal shamans (medicine men) called on "the bear" to attend curing rituals. The shaman would then pull on gloves made from bear paws to impersonate the animal and, according to tribal belief, would then become "the bear" with all its healing capabilities. It was further believed that the shaman could transform himself into a real bear in the same manner that a bear could transform itself into a man. After his death, the shaman lived with the bears in the spirit world.

These tribes also believed that the bear had given to them a powerful medicine, almost a cure-all, the aster root. It was called "bear root" or "bear medicine." During curing ceremonies the shaman chewed the bear root and went into a trancelike state which enabled him to see the witch causing the illness.

A fairly common and widespread Indian legend is about a lost child found in the woods by a she-bear and reared with her own cubs. Eventually the bear-raised boy returns to his people with messages from the bears concerning the sincerity of the Indians' prayers which the bears hear and reply to.

Another typical legend involves a young Indian woman who has a bear as a lover. The usual outcome is for the girl's family to kill the animal, whereupon she turns into a bear herself.

A similar plot is seen in the stories wherein an Indian brave has a bear for a wife. She refuses to help the Indian community in its food gathering and preparation. But, when the supply of food is exhausted the bear wife miraculously reveals an underground store of dried salmon and berries, and the village has food for the winter. The ending is not happy, however. The Indian brave meets a former sweetheart, and when his bear wife sees them together she takes her child, who turns into a bear, and goes away. The husband follows, but he is unable to find them.

The black bear's winter sleep seemed to mystify early explorers. In fact, many people are still puzzled by it, and some of the odd beliefs that came out of the mystery of hibernation are around today. Black bears were discovered asleep in their winter dens holding forepaws in their mouths. This led to the erroneous belief that in this manner bears obtained nourishment from their paws and were sustained during the winter sleep. In some cases the explanation went on to reason that since the bear had four paws and each paw was capable of providing sustenance for one month, the bear could hibernate for four months.

Another belief that still appears to have some adherents in this country is that the bear cub comes into the world a shapeless, unrecognizable mass of flesh without face or limbs. By constant licking the mother bear shapes it up into a proper bear cub.

The bear's abbreviated tail is explained by an ancient European folk tale in which a certain long-tailed bear was persuaded by a fox to fish with its tail through a hole in the ice one winter day. The tail froze in the ice, and thereupon the fox, which did not like bears, proceeded to

45

A large brown male from Yellowstone National Park. Note the poor excuse for a tail.

A black bear takes it easy.

attack. The bear, in its great struggle to escape, wrenched itself free but broke off its tail in doing so. Thus, it has had a short tail ever since.

Another bear story, considered to be fiction by some writers on the subject, advises that the proper procedure to follow if one is attacked by a bear is to lie face down on the ground and hold one's breath. The bear, believing its victim is dead, will then go away. While this has all the earmarks of being just another bear story, there is, in my opinion, some reasonable basis for such an action. I don't think carnivorous animals have a concept of killing when they attack but only of destroying their prey's ability to resist or escape. A lion does not necessarily kill a zebra before it starts to eat it. It knocks the zebra down, and as soon as it stops moving or fighting back, further attack is unnecessary. The same thing could hold true for the bear. If the quarry lies motionless, there would be no reason to continue an attack. The bear might or might not go away, but it seems unlikely that a bear or any other carnivore would punish a dormant body simply because some tiny spark of life might remain.

I don't think a carnivore can tell when an animal is dead, but only that it no longer resists. I do not think the concept of dead prey means anything to it, and it bites and mauls only until the prey quits trying to escape.

This old bear slept this way for almost an hour in the middle of the afternoon and seemed completely unconcerned about several other bears that passed nearby during his nap.

Spring

AFTER TWO TO FOUR MONTHS—depending upon weather conditions—spent in deep winter sleep, black bears emerge from their dens into a world filled with the restless stirrings of things wanting to grow. Mountain streams, swollen by the melting snow, hurry toward the waiting valleys below. Troubled spring skies are etched with wavy lines of migrating geese leisurely following the growing warmth northward. Deer leave their hard-used winter ranges and follow the receding snow line as it moves toward higher elevations with its promise of a coming food abundance.

For much of our wildlife, spring is a time for migration from winter range to summer range. But this is not true for the black bear. Usually it has slept through lean winter months blissfully unaware of winter's hardships. It is New Year's Day for a black bear whenever it wakes up in the spring. This is generally in March, although weather seems to affect the date, and bears in the deep snow country of the north may emerge from their dens later than those in southern areas. The first bears out in the spring are nearly always full-grown males. Females and cubs emerge some time later.

After its long winter's sleep, the black bear seems to wake slowly over a period of several days. When it first emerges from the den, its movements are lazy. The animal appears dazed and half asleep. It may wander aimlessly about for a while or just sit by the mouth of the den. It does not seem to be either very thirsty or hungry when it awakes and may neither eat nor drink the first time out. After only a half hour or so it may return to its den.

48

When black bears first emerge from their winter dens they awaken slowly, and it may be some time before they are ready for food and water. However, they are in surprisingly good physical condition despite their long fast.

In one reported observation, a bear stayed inside for another two days before coming out again. On this second occasion, the bear left the den for good and broke its long fast with a little water, some willow twigs and grass, and the contents of an ant hill.

In another instance, a group of loggers observed a large black bear when it appeared on the opposite side of a stream from them. It seemed unconcerned with their presence and walked to the stream within 30 yards of the watchers where it drank for a long time. Three times it lowered its head to the stream until it was fairly bursting from the amount of water consumed. Then it waded the stream and walked past the men, gazing about in a dazed manner as if it were still half asleep.

Observations of captive black bears indicate that the animals resume normal feeding activity within three days to a week after coming out of their winter's sleep. Oddly enough, when they leave their dens in the spring, their physical condition is about the same as it was when they went into the dens in the fall.

Weight loss during the winter sleep is minor. It seems to be greatest in the spring due to the sparse feed available and eaten during those early spring weeks after waking.

Victor H. Cahalane, in speaking of the female with cubs in the early spring, says: "It is generally presumed that her fatty layer is spongy and that the cells are mere shells. According to this theory she shrinks rapidly and two or three weeks later is lean and ravenously hungry again."

The cubs are born in January and February after a gestation period of about seven months, and it is doubtful that the female is aware of the event. For many years there was considerable mystery about the breeding and gestation period of black bears, because hunters were unable to find embryos in fall-killed female bears. In those days, some people believed that breeding occurred after the bears went into their dens in the winter.

Now we know that mating occurs in June or early July, but the fertilized ovum does not immediately attach itself to the walls of the uterus, as it does in most mammals, to commence its fetal development. This is called "delayed implantation" and probably occurs, in black bears, in November. The fertilized egg remains free and undeveloped in the female's body cavity and does not implant itself to start growth until approximately four months after mating.

By early December, the embryo will be about .7 inch long and weigh approximately .0015 pound. The head, mouth, tongue, feet, and tail, as well as other organs and appendates, are well-developed at this time. With only 30 per cent of the gestation period remaining, the embryo must develop rapidly, since it will increase in weight from 300 to 500 times before the normal birth date in late January or early February; this accelerated growth will, chiefly, enlarge structures already formed.

Newborn black bear cubs are 8 inches long and weigh from 6 to 10 ounces. This is about 1/500 of the weight of the mother, the smallest weight ratio of newborn to mother of any animal except marsupials. In humans the ratio is 1:20, and in porcupines 1:15. In fact, a newborn porcupine is actually larger and heavier than a newborn black bear. It has been suggested that because the mother bear must often nurse her cubs three and possibly four months with no food for herself, they have to be small. If they were 1/20 as large as the mother and weighed 10 to 15 pounds, the mother might easily starve in the den.

The squirrel-sized cubs, which have been described as resembling miniature, almost legless, bulldogs, are covered with a coat of fine black hair so thin they look naked. They are blind, toothless, and have undeveloped ears. Matson describes four-day-old cubs as looking "like tan colored pigs about the size of a rat."

While the litter size of black bears may vary from one to five, two is most usual. Triplets are not at all rare, but quadruplets are seldom seen. Five cubs in a litter is exceptional, and there is always some question as to whether or not these represent combined litters. There is one recorded instance of a female that had six small cubs of equal size with her when she was shot. She weighed 225 pounds and was extremely emaciated.

51

This black bear cub, taken from a den, was estimated to be about two months old. It was unable to stand and moved about with a sort of flat-bellied crawl.

The first-born is almost always a solitary cub, but after the female is four years old, she generally has twins.

Although the available information on the subject is meager, the indications are that cub litters contain more males than females. This was substantiated by a sex ratio study of 240 black bears taken by hunters in Colorado—of these, 52.5 per cent were males. It has been suggested that more males might be so taken, because they travel extensively and thus expose themselves to more hazards than the females do.

It is generally assumed that the pregnant female bear is either in deep sleep at the time the cubs are born, or so drowsy that she may be

A female black bear usually has only one cub during her first breeding season; thereafter, she is apt to have twins.

only vaguely aware that the cubs have arrived. Matson, in reporting on a denning female kept under observation from December 6 to March 23 noted that on the day before her cubs were born the female walked out of the den for about 15 feet, scratched herself, and then after an unknown interval of time, went back into the den. The blind and helpless cubs find their way to the mother's teats and alternately feed and sleep nestled in the warmth of the mother's fur during the remainder of the sleeping period.

The black bear has two groups of teats, two inguinal and four pectoral. There is a possibility that the inguinal teats are used during the

53

A seven-month-old cub nursing.

den life and the pectoral after the young are able to follow. However, in the case of the female with six cubs following her (mentioned previously), all six teats were full of milk.

Cubs continue to nurse until well into the summer. Although they undoubtedly begin to nibble on other available foods as soon as they leave the den and become increasingly more proficient at feeding themselves as summer progresses, the female doesn't usually wean them entirely until some time in August.

The female most often nurses her cubs while sitting down if she has no more than three. In this position she is able to keep her head erect and can observe what goes on around her. She may lean against a log or tree trunk or against the branches of a bush. Sometimes she will support the cubs with her forelegs in near-human fashion. When there are

54

four or more cubs, the female reclines on her back and tries awkwardly to hold her head erect. Black bear quadruplets seen in 1939 in Sequoia National Park, California, were observed to take the same relative positions each time they nursed. It has been reported that cubs hum as they feed, but though I have watched nursing cubs from as close as 50 feet, I have not heard this sound. Possibly, it was too low to hear from that distance.

Not much is known about the care given cubs by the mother during hibernation. Since there is little that the cubs are inclined to do other than snuggle into the mother's warm fur and eat or sleep, about all the female has to guard against is rolling on her young. It would appear that she manages very well, although at times the dens occupied by a mother bear and her cubs are so small it seems impossible for the female to move about, let alone turn over or turn around, without injuring the helpless cubs.

By the time cubs are a couple of weeks old their coats have developed to such an extent that they cover them completely with fine downlike fur. M. P. Skinner, in his report on the bears in Yellowstone National Park, stated: "All the cubs I have ever seen at this stage of their lives have been black, but many of them gradually change their tint and become lighter colored. . . ." There is a similarity here between newborn black bear cubs and newborn bobcats and coyotes. They too are born quite dark, almost black, and then gradually become lighter-colored.

The feet of a black bear cub are pink and like a human baby's. Although the time seems to vary among individuals, cubs generally open their eyes at forty days and cut their first teeth at the same time. By then they may weigh a couple of pounds and measure a foot in length. The hind legs are still practically useless, and about all the cub can do is push itself ahead. In reporting on the development of captive cubs, Bertrand E. Smith said: "When they tried to get anywhere, they

55

pushed themselves along very much like a baby first starting to creep. When they were first able to crawl, it was never in a straight line, always in a circle, and then they toppled over helplessly."

It has been suggested that this long period of weakness in cubs' legs is nature's way of preventing them from crawling away from their mother and out of the den during the period that she is asleep.

Even though cubs open their eyes at forty days, observations have indicated that until about twelve weeks their ability to focus the eyes and to distinguish even large moving objects is notably poor. During this period they apparently rely upon their nose and ears for direction.

With the coming of the warm winds of spring, the bright sunshine, and the melting snow, there is an increased restlessness within the dens. The female frequently turns and changes position, and the cubs may totter to the entrance for a confused and myopic look at the bright outside world. If the weather stays warm the mother will finally stretch herself and move outside the den. On this initial exit she may venture outside for a few feet and remain only a short time before going back in to her cubs. But an awakening appetite will soon bring her outside again where she will pick over the offerings of "spring tonic." This generally consists of green grass, a few cedar twigs, and herbs. The female may emerge alone for several days; but then, if weather and ground conditions are not too severe, she will bring the cubs out with her. By this time the little ones will weigh around 5 pounds and will have developed hard claws suitable for climbing. They are still awkward and unsteady on their feet, however, and stumble and fall over obstacles in their paths as they follow the mother bear about. They are quick to try their claws on available trees, and climbing appears to be something they do instinctively.

When a mature bear first leaves its den in the spring, its coat is in prime condition, but begins to deteriorate immediately. About a month after coming from the winter den or by early summer, the bear

Spring

begins to shed its fur. The shedding is accompanied by much itching, and the itching by much scratching. One of the most amusing sights one can see in the woods is that of an old boar black bear going through elaborate contortions to get just the right spot in position against a convenient tree. Then he slowly rubs the offending portion of skin across the rough bark and assumes a look of sublime bliss and contentment. As the old coat gradually falls out it may hang in shreds and give the bear a ragged, moth-eaten appearance. The fur starts to go first on the legs and belly, and a bear helps it come off and relieve his itching, by straddling bushes and small trees on his walks through the woods.

The pelage of the black bear consists of a dense inner layer of short hair, called the undercoat, and an outer layer of longer coarser guard hairs. The furry coat forms an insulating covering and the hairs are associated with glands which supply an oily secretion that keeps them waterproof. Thus the animal is protected against rain and cold. The process of shedding the old fur and growing new is naturally timed so that the bear has the thinnest coat during the warmest part of the summer. New hair slowly replaces the old and by late August becomes quite noticeable. The animal's coat takes on a sleek glossy appearance,

Twin cubs photographed on June 1. They were agile and quick at this time.

A shedding black bear can look very ragged in the middle of the summer. This animal was a brown color phase. The old hair was light blond, but the new growth was a rich cinnamon color. I doubt that this was a color change of pelage. It seems more likely that the light color of the old hair was due to age and weathering.

This big black bear arched his back against the rough bark of a tree for a long, luxurious scratching session. I observed other bears using this tree for the same purpose.

This young bear has suspended his scratching momentarily to see what the photographer is doing. Then he walks over and straddles a small tree to relieve the itching on his belly.

Spring

and as fall marches toward winter the fur gets longer, glossier, and dense, until by the time the bear is ready for hibernation it is in prime condition.

Food presents no problem to young cubs when they follow their mother out of the den. Although they may nibble at plants and investigate crawling insects, they will continue to nurse for some time. Finding food is not so easy for yearlings and mature bears. After a long winter's inactivity, a bear's digestive tract awakes slowly. About ten days are required for it to return to normal functioning. In one case, a captive bear—weighing substantially the same before and after hibernation—ate its first solid food four days after emerging from its den.

Since the animal has used up little of its fat during the winter's inactivity, it has something to sustain it during these early spring days when food is not plentiful. A drink of water seems to be the first consideration for a stomach that has not functioned all winter. This may be followed by a bit of grass, a few willow twigs, possibly some snow lilies, various starchy plants, and skunk cabbage. The inner cambium layer of bark of pine or fir trees is a preferred delicacy. As the snow retreats, carcasses of winter-killed animals are exposed for bears who have become increasingly hungry. Their winter store of fat disappears rapidly in the spring. The first ants, beetles, and grubs appear at lower elevations, and on the warm slopes bursting buds, early roots, and fresh mountain herbs provide food. Bears may follow spring into the

A black bear feeding on spring grass.

The World of the Black Bear

higher elevations. As the snow line climbs the mountains, it reveals additional preserved winter-killed animals for them to feed upon. Thus the black bear manages through the spring and into mid-June when the weather warms, food becomes plentiful, and the living is easy.

Aside from mated pairs and females with cubs, black bears have little to do with other members of their tribe. They are basically loners and seem to avoid close contact with other bears. If one bear happens upon a group in a preferred feeding area, for example, it will give no sign of being aware of the other animals. Nor will those that were there first recognize this newcomer's presence. Yet, it is obvious that these animals with their sensitive ears and noses must be aware of each other.

At different times, I have observed black bears near refuse pits in various national parks. While this is not like watching them entirely unaffected by the presence of humans, I do not believe the relation-

Mature bears seldom get this close to each other. These acted completely indifferent to the presence of the other.

ship between bears would vary much under any circumstances. At times I could see as many as a dozen bears around the pit. Several times I noticed a bear suddenly look off into the woods in an alert manner, and although I could see nothing myself another animal would emerge from the spot within a few minutes. I am sure the bear could not see what was coming any better than I could, but it knew. Also, I have seen bears sprawled comfortably across a log get up unhurriedly and stroll off 20 or 30 yards to lie down again. Although these bears gave no sign of the reason for the move, invariably, when I looked there was another bear approaching the vacated spot. Generally, all small bears are wary of large ones.

I saw one of the strangest sights of this kind at a small, remote refuse dump in Yellowstone National Park on June 2, 1964. A mature black bear was feeding on the refuse when I noticed a younger one approaching. This newcomer was a two- or three-year-old animal, I would guess, and noticeably smaller than the first. As the smaller drew near, it began to bawl like a cow in pain. It came in slowly, its head close to the ground in apparent supplication. It seemed to be saying, "You're bigger than I am and I know it. You can run me off if you want to, but I'm starving to death. Please let me eat!"

Whatever the actual meaning of the crying, it was effective, and the larger bear left the smaller one alone. All the time that they were eating together, the smaller one kept up a constant bawling and moaning. It seemed apparent that the smaller animal was fully aware that black bears in general are short tempered and inconsistent. In fact, it displayed a bit of this characteristic itself when the larger animal, its appetite satisfied for the moment, started to leave the area. The smaller one growled and made several menacing steps toward the departing bear, but with no effect whatsoever.

Bears don't actually fight very much, but they do a lot of bluffing—against people as well as other bears. They show their teeth, bellow and roar, make false lunges at their opponents, and slap the ground with a mighty thud. When two large bears engage in such antics, one could reasonably expect to see some epic struggle, but what usually happens is that one bear gets outbluffed. The loser moves aside carefully, still threatening, and slowly makes off, unharmed but with its self-respect intact.

However, when bears do fight, it is truly a battle of giants. Most frequently altercations are between rival males during courting periods. Their fights are regular brawls and are accompanied by a great amount of roaring and bawling. They may fight on all fours, but they are more likely to stand erect. In this position they land heavy powerful blows with their forepaws. Or they grasp their opponent and hold him close so they can bite him about the jaws and throat. They do not, contrary to some popular opinion, attempt to hug an enemy and squeeze him to death. Despite the strength of the animals and the ferocity of their attack, there is often surprisingly little damage done. In the first place, bears are tough animals, covered, except around the face, with a heavy protective coat of fur. Secondly, most of their blows land on the head and shoulders, where they do comparatively little damage. Much of the fighting is more like wrestling. A thrown bear is a defeated bear. He usually acknowledges defeat immediately by trying to get away as quickly as possible.

Nonetheless, the black bear is an exceptionally powerful and rugged animal. In 1956 at the winter quarters in Florida of the Ringling Brothers Circus, a Maine black bear and an African lion were being trained for an act together. The trainer turned away for a moment and the lion jumped the bear, ripping its shoulder open. The bear reared up and hit the lion a mighty blow with a forepaw. The big cat went backward for several feet and nearly had its shoulder torn off. The lion was injured so badly it had to be destroyed, but the bear was ready to go back to work within a few days.

The only two fights I have witnessed were each between a male and a female in defense of the cubs. They both occurred in Crater Lake

Spring

National Park. In each case I was able to watch from the beginning and see the action develop. The first fight was between a large brown female that had been feeding in a refuse pit with her two small brown cubs and a large black male. This was in July, and the cubs would have been 5½ to 6 months old. Prior to the arrival of the female, I had watched the large black male go into a patch of evergreens about 50 yards away and lie down.

The female and cubs fed on the refuse for thirty minutes or so, and then the female climbed out and lumbered off in a direction away from the hidden male. Right behind her was one of the cubs. The other, delayed, no doubt, by something interesting it had found, did not come out of the pit until after the female was out of sight.

The tiny brown cub finally clambered out of the pit and paused on the edge in obvious confusion. I would have thought the cub could have followed its mother's scent easily, but perhaps their previous travels about the pit and the scent of many other bears confused the youngster. In any event, instead of following its mother, it galloped off in the direction of the hidden male. As it passed by the thicket, the cub either saw or smelled the male and turned to investigate, probably to see if it was its mother.

As it got close, it saw its mistake and turned to run, but too late. The old male grabbed the cub by a hind leg. The frightened cub let out a frantic bawl of pain. Moments later the female came charging through the underbrush, but 30 yards from the male and cub, she turned back. I couldn't be sure, but I think she suddenly realized she'd left the other cub unprotected and went to put it up a tree where it would be safe. She then came running back and dived into the thicket from which the pained bawls of the other cub were coming.

There was no bluffing this time. She jumped the old male immediately. He turned the cub loose, and it came running directly toward me dragging a hind leg that looked broken and climbed about 15 feet up a small evergreen tree 10 yards from me with a speed that was

63

amazing, considering it had only three sound legs. Meanwhile, the male and female were going after each other. They would stand and grapple, filling the woods with their roaring and growling. There had been several other bears around the area, including a couple of yearlings and several mature animals. The instant the fight started, they all ran away or climbed trees.

Although the two bears were in full view for several minutes, the action was so fast I couldn't tell which was winning. Part of the time they battled erect and part on all fours. Bushes were torn up and a cloud of pumice dust partially obscured my view of the fight. I was standing out in the open watching this battle of roaring and bellowing titans, and I must confess that, with all the noise, movement, noncombatant bears running for cover, and raw savagery, I was so overwhelmed I was unable to remember many of the details of the fight.

They finally moved away so I could no longer see the action because of the intervening trees and brush, but I could hear the roaring. They must have been 100 yards away when the fight ended. I was unable to determine which animal had broken away, but I suspect that the male had finally decided he'd had enough.

The female came hurrying back to see about her cubs. She came to the tree that the wounded cub had climbed, swinging her head and moaning, and peered into the branches where the youngster was perched as if she was trying to determine if it was all right. Off in the distance the other cub whimpered, and the mother bear turned and ran toward the sound. In less than a half-minute she was back again, pacing around the tree and occasionally standing up against the trunk. She seemed to be trying to get the youngster to come down.

Twice more she went away in answer to the whimpering cries of the unharmed cub, and then brought it back with her. Somehow, she managed to climb the little tree and work her way through the small branches to inspect the hurt cub at close range. I did not quite see how she managed this, for the trunk was not much more than 6 inches in

64

A female and two cubs a few minutes before the female attacked a big male to protect her cubs.

diameter. Even then the cub would not come down. The mother bear was obviously quite upset and appeared to be at a loss for some way to get it out of the tree. About that time one of the park refuse trucks drove into the area with a great clattering and banging of garbage cans. This was too much for the cub. It came scrambling down out of the tree, falling the last 7 feet, and took off after its mother and twin, running on three legs.

I reported the incident to the park rangers and checked with them several times later in the summer. No one ever saw the female and her cubs again so I was unable to learn whether or not the wound to the cub was fatal. In all probability the cub recovered, even though it might be always a little lame, but the female must have moved them a considerable distance into what she considered a safer area.

65

The two cubs followed their mother into the refuse pit.

This cub, late in following its mother and twin, was attacked by an old male that had been resting in a nearby thicket.

Safe in a tree, the cubs watched the battle between their mother and the trespassing old male.

When the fights started, other bears in the area, such as this two-and-a-half-year-old, either left or climbed trees.

The female (left) opens her attack on the male.

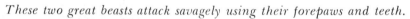

These two great beasts attack savagely using their forepaws and teeth.

The female (left) gets the advantage and strikes at the male.

This semi-healed wound on the old male's head a month after the fight is evidence of the ferocity of the female's attack.

The World of the Black Bear

The second fight I observed occurred in the same area but under different circumstances. A female with twin cubs was in the refuse pit feeding. There were a dozen or more bears scattered about awaiting their turn at the garbage, but they weren't inclined to argue with the feeding trio. A short time later a large and grumpy old male I had seen many times sauntered in from the woods. The pit was too deep for him to see the feeding occupants. He walked up and stuck his head over the edge and into trouble. With a great roar the female came up out of the pit and at him. The two cubs went out the other side like overgrown jack rabbits and streaked up the nearest tree. All the other bears in the vicinity decided they had pressing business elsewhere. For a few moments there were bears going in all directions. A two-year-old was in such a hurry to climb a nearby tree that it almost ran over me, and I was so engrossed in the action that I paid no attention to it until after the fight was over.

The female had the advantage of surprise and almost knocked the big male off his feet with her first charge. They fought on all fours and standing up, but the male never really had a chance. As soon as he could, he broke off the fight and retreated. Some time later the male came back and walked by within 3 feet of where I was sitting in the car. High on his left cheek was a bleeding 2-inch gash which had apparently been inflicted by the irate female, but it didn't seem to bother him.

The mother bear has the entire responsibility of rearing the cubs. The male bear leaves the female soon after mating and thereafter takes no part in family life. It is doubtful that by the time the cubs appear on the scene in the spring the male even remembers his mate. He is certainly unaware of any relationship to the cubs. In fact, the father might well constitute the greatest menace to cubs.

However, the youngsters have little to fear from other wild animals as long as the mother bear is about. There are few animals other than the rare grizzly that would dare attack mature female black bears. Nevertheless, one of the first things a female teaches her cubs is to climb a tree and to climb it fast and without question when she grunts the signal to start climbing. Should they hesitate too long, she cuffs them severely, and they know better next time. Also, she does not permit them to come down until the danger is well past or until she says so. Once in a tree they are comparatively safe for they can retreat to the ends of branches and small upper limbs where heavy adult bears and other large predators cannot follow.

Cubs quickly become very much at home in trees. They show no fear at all of heights and demonstrate great agility in their climbing.

After the fight, the female brought the two cubs down from the tree.

Triplets are not uncommon among black bears.

A female with twins—the usual thing after the bear's first breeding cycle.

Spring

Seven-month-old cubs in a tree waiting for their mother's command to come down. The second one is almost completely hidden by the needles.

The cubs stay in the tree until summoned by the mother. This may cover a period of several hours and in such cases a cub may find a comfortable limb, drape himself over it, and go to sleep.

In the instance previously described (where the female thought her cubs were threatened and attacked the male) the cubs remained up a tree for about two hours; they slept about one hour during that time. After the fight was over, the female lay down to rest under the tree containing the cubs. I watched constantly, but if any signal was given to the cubs to come down, I failed to see or hear it. It seemed as if she just waited until they were ready to come down, but this was probably because I failed to recognize the "down" message.

Probably a cub's greatest enemy is man, mostly because of the fear mature bears have of him. There are many records of females deserting their cubs in the dens because of too much human disturbance.

In studies of black bears where live-trapping of cubs was required, the female bears did not display strong maternal protective instincts and quickly abandoned cubs when danger was imminent. In two cases the females attempted to frighten away the handling crew by rushing

73

This bear has found something it likes in the end of this old rotten log—probably insects of some kind.

at them snorting and champing their teeth, but approached no closer than 10 feet. Loud shouting by the handling crew seemed to unnerve the attacking bears, causing them to terminate their charges.

The female bear is actually a very good mother to her young. In addition to always being ready to defend them—except in cases where man is involved, as described—she is a stern disciplinarian as well as an indulgent parent. Education starts soon after they leave the den. Probably the first thing they learn is to obey the mother bear, and the second thing is to climb trees. After safety, comes the problem of feeding themselves, and the mother soon begins to teach them to hunt mice and squirrels, to find fruit and other food, and to swim.

When they are not learning, the youngsters work off their surplus energy in play. This consists mostly of wrestling with each other in mock combat, or biting and mauling the patient mother bear.

I watched a female with two small cubs resting in the shade on a warm July day. The cubs were not a bit tired, and so they wrestled and played tag around the mother. One of the cubs kept climbing over her to get at the other cub, but she showed no concern at all.

Although the black bear is classified as a carnivore, it is omnivorous. As a matter of fact, this animal consumes considerably more vegetable matter than it does animal matter. A study of the seasonal food habits of black bears in Maine showed these results:

	Spring	*Summer*	*Fall*	*All Year*
Vegetable matter, %	59.1	80.1	48.8	76.7
Animal matter, including insects, %	33.0	4.9	13.9	8.1
Trash and debris, %	7.9	15.0	37.3	15.2
Total	100.0	100.0	100.0	100.0

It has been said that a bear eats flesh like a wolf, grass like an ox, fish like an otter, carrion like a coyote, bugs like a hen, and berries like a bird. A black bear will eat almost anything. It seems to have a truly catholic taste to go along with its enormous appetite and relishes the warm freshness of newly killed meat along with the aromatic ripeness of carrion. Honey and the sweetness of wild berries are great favorites of the black bear, but during certain seasons the animal seems to like equally well the acid juice of skunk cabbage and the alumlike taste of bitter cherries.

Since the range of the black bear extends all the way from Alaska to southern Florida it is to be expected that there will be some variation in diets. However, it seems to be only in the specifics rather than in general classifications that the omnivorous diet of the black bear shows any variation, except that northern animals appear to eat more flesh.

During the summer the black bear lives well. A plethora of insects

The World of the Black Bear

along with ripening berries are the staples of warm-weather meals. For variety, the animal occasionally digs out a woodchuck or some other rodent, sweetens its diet with a raid on a honey-laden bee tree whenever it can find one, and occasionally visits some nearby garbage dump.

Included on the black bear's menu of insect delicacies are such items as ants, ant eggs, Mayflies, yellow-jackets, bees, grasshoppers, crickets, scale insects, maggots, pandora moth pupae and eggs, hornets, beetles, and grubs. A black bear likes nothing better than to stir up an ant nest and let the angry insects swarm on its paws; then it licks them off.

This animal is picking at some bit of discovered food with front claws and incisors.

A mature bear searchs through refuse for food.

A yearling, wary of larger bears, heads for cover with a prized food item.

The World of the Black Bear

All kinds of fruit and berries are relished. A bear can, if it wishes, delicately pick berries one by one without getting any leaves. However, it generally just strips the entire limb and eats leaves, twigs, and berries.

Bears are not especially efficient eaters and will often swallow, along with their food, extraneous material such as stones, mud, sticks, cones, and needles. I have watched bears feeding on refuse consume numerous servings of paper that had, apparently, held food at one time and still retained an appetizing smell. On occasion a bear will straddle a small fruit tree and ride it down to where the fruit can be reached. Or, on larger trees, it may tear off limbs to get at the fruit.

During the fall months a black bear consumes great quantities of acorns, beechnuts, and chestnuts, wherever these are found. When it can find them, it takes pine and fir seeds gathered and stored by hard-working squirrels. When eating nuts, shells and all are consumed. A black bear seems always to be in the mood for a meal of honey, honeycomb, and bees. It will rob a natural bee tree wherever it can find one, or if given the opportunity, will take apart domestic hives. Bears are protected by a tough hide and thick fur except on the nose and face. Here they are susceptible to stings of angry bees trying to protect their hives. Undoubtedly, inexperienced bears get more stings than old-timers at stealing honey, but despite their loud bawls of pain they scoop up the honey and eat it comb and all. Bees and larvae consumed with the honey add additional flavor.

Black bears seldom kill a large animal for food. This is generally thought to be due to the bear's sheer inability to capture the fleeter prey animals. Consequently, a bear is contented to kill and eat such minor game as porcupines, woodchucks, cottontail rabbits, small rodents, frogs, and the like.

Other than the occasional small burrowing animal black bears intentionally dig out, they find most of their rodent tidbits more or less by accident. When they search for insects under stones and logs, they sometimes discover a mouse or a squirrel and flatten it with a quick

78

Young yellow bellied marmots (illustrated) along with the woodchuck and Hoary marmot are found in black bear country and are captured and eaten at times.

Golden Mantled ground squirrels are thick in much of the western range of the black bear and may provide some food for it. However, I have seen them running about near black bears without creating much excitement.

Although the black bear occasionally feeds on porcupines, a careless bear may get its face and mouth full of quills. Death by starvation results.

swat of the paw. Bears have a well-defined and most efficient method of turning stones. They slip a front paw under the near edge of the stone and skillfully flip it over and away from them. Quickly, then, they dip their head and with their long tongue gather in the insects, reptiles, or rodents that have taken refuge under the stone to avoid the hot sun. During the spring, a bear will occasionally stumble onto a deer fawn or a moose or elk calf and, of course, it doesn't pass up such an easy meal.

On rare occasions a bear may develop a taste for horses, cows, sheep, and pigs. This taste often results in some destructive attacks on domestic stock. One toothless old bear is reported to have killed twenty-six sheep in one day. It kept fat on its prey as did another predator bear that had a fondness for the udders of nursing ewes. However, black bears probably obtain most of the meat and fish of their diet from carrion, some of it in a badly decomposed condition. When feeding on a carcass, either fresh or otherwise, they peel the hide back from the flesh as they go along. When they have finished, all that is left is the hide with feet and head attached.

Cannibalism is not too common among bears, although this might be the case simply because black bears find others too difficult a prey if they are of equal size, and too wary if small. However, there are records of bears killing and eating other black bears as well as eating some killed by other means. It has also been found that black bears can be readily baited to a trap by a carcass of their own kind.

Although a black bear will eat almost anything that is animal or vegetable, it undoubtedly has its preferred foods. Observations of feeding bears and studies of stomach contents have led to some conclusions relative to preferred foods which may possibly be in error. Certain foods instead of being preferred, as commonly thought, may in reality be only subsistence foods. In some fairly recent studies of methods of live-trapping black bears, it was discovered that the most consistently successful bait was fresh venison. Carcasses of lesser domestic and wild mammals and fish were not as effective. Pit baits of offal and

80

fresh fish were seldom eaten, though bears frequently wallowed in them. Table garbage was effective, but negligible success was achieved with honey, molasses, sorghum, apples, or peanut butter. Bears showed a distinct aversion to putrid flesh baits. After several days in a trap, baits became fetid or infested with maggots and were ineffective.

The bulk of a bear's diet is vegetable matter, which does not contain the concentrated nutrition that flesh does so the animal is constantly busy searching for food to sustain the needs of its massive body. The amount consumed in a twenty-four-hour period by an average black bear will undoubtedly vary with the season and the kind of food that is available. But the quantities eaten by captive bears offer an indication of daily requirements. In one case this consisted of 3 pounds of butterfish, 4 pounds of horse meat, 3 loaves of bread, and apples, carrots, celery, etc., as available. Since fish, meat, and bread represent concentrated foods, it would obviously take a great deal more of random vegetable matter to sustain a bear.

Summer

JUNE BRINGS SOME RATHER DRASTIC CHANGES into the lives of most black bears. Females with new cubs are busy teaching them to stay out of trouble (a thing that is difficult for a black bear, and especially a cub, to do) and taking advantage of nature's bountiful summer table to show them how to find food. Two-year-olds face their first complete year of being self-sufficient at that difficult age when they are neither cub nor adult.

They no longer have the protection of their mothers and yet are not large enough to defend themselves against mature bears or large predators. In feeding areas where other bears may be present, they must wait at a safe distance or up a tree until all larger bears have taken the choicest portions.

However, their situation is not nearly as bad as that which yearlings face. A cub goes through its first year with its mother. When there is something to be learned, she is there to teach it. This includes preparing for the cub's first winter and going into the den. The female spends this first winter with her year-old cubs and stays with them through the lean and difficult days of the following spring.

But now it is time for the female to mate again. During the first half of June her interest in a male bear replaces her affection for her cubs. The cubs will be reluctant to leave, but eventually maternal indifference and intimidation by her new mate will force the yearling cubs to move on. They may travel together for another year and then,

82

A female with cubs of the year. She will not breed as long as these small cubs are with her.

A female (rear) with one-and-a-half-year-old cubs. This is the first of June, and she will soon force them to leave as it is time for her to breed again.

One-and-a-half-year-old bears that have just been forced out on their own. They seem a little dubious about losing the protection and guidance of their mothers.

when they are around two and one-half years old, part company to become loners like the older bears.

The female mates for the first time at the age of three and one-half years and every second year thereafter, unless she loses her cubs in the spring prior to mating time. Under such circumstances she will mate again on successive years.

Presumably because of the stimulus of suckling the young, ovulation is inhibited and thus there is an alternate year breeding cycle. However, when cubs have been withheld from a female for as little as two days, thus creating an interrupted lactation, the female has come into oestrus, conceived, and delivered cubs the following year. Captive black bears will breed in consecutive years when cubs are removed before the normal breeding season. One captive female had thirteen litters in seventeen years—a total of thirty-four cubs.

While it is fairly well established that the breeding age of female black bear is three and one-half years, there is still some question about the male. Recent studies indicate that he rarely reaches sexual maturity during the third year of life. The consensus of opinion seems to be that both male and female breed at approximately three and one-half years.

On June 4, 1964, in Yellowstone Park, I observed a big brown male bear and a black female, only slightly smaller, traveling together. Their size and general appearance led me to estimate their ages at five years or more, for they were certainly well-matured animals. It was obvious that the male was in a most romantic mood. The female showed more interest in food than in romance, but seemed to have no objection to the close companionship of the male. Both accepted some offerings of bread from a passing motorist, but then left while there was still some bread on the ground and headed across country. A couple of miles farther on, I saw them again, crossing a meadow fresh and green in spring grass. The female was leading; the male followed

50 feet or so behind. In a boggy portion of the meadow, where the grass was especially lush, they stopped and grazed.

I went on another two or three miles to a small, out-of-the-way refuse pit I knew of, to observe any bears that might be feeding there. After about thirty minutes the amorous pair came up over the hill. The female kept busy investigating all the food possibilities, but the male showed only occasional interest in eating. Most of the time while the two were in the vicinity, the male just lay down and watched the female.

For at least ten minutes during this time the male bear was lying so close to the car in which I was sitting that I could have reached out the window and scratched his ears. He seemed unconcerned about my presence. When the female finally tired of the spot, the male obediently followed her away.

The fact that they left available food unconsumed and resumed eating again a few minutes later, only to quit and move again indicated a restlessness which may have been connected in some way with their breeding activities.

This observation tends to indicate that the courting of the female by the male begins early in June but that it is sometimes later before the female is ready to receive the male. Most authorities agree that actual mating occurs during June and the early part of July. The male and female stay together for about a month, and during this time the pair demonstrate great devotion to one another. They may stand erect and hug and paw each other fondly, or wrestle for fun.

Bears are considered to be monogamous on a year-to-year basis. That is, a mated pair are faithful during their brief one-month summer "marriage," but afterward they separate and probably forget all about their respective mates. The following summer the female with her cubs will not mate, and the male will find a different female receptive to his attentions.

During the mating period the males may have to fight fierce battles to retain possession of females. There seems to be a tendency for the female to stay with her first choice even though a larger and more powerful male might attempt to interfere. It would appear, however, that if this interloper is sufficiently strong and persistent, the female might have no choice but to accept a new mate or to share her attentions.

A female will produce young until she is about twenty years old. After her first cub, born when she is four years old, the general rule is twins every other year or an average of one cub a year. Thus the average lifetime reproduction potential of a female black bear is about seventeen or eighteen cubs.

The black bear has forty-two teeth, but the total number is seldom present in adults. The smaller premolars are frequently lost with age. The dental formula is:

$$I\frac{3}{3} \quad C\frac{1}{1} \quad P\frac{4}{4} \quad M\frac{2}{3}$$

This means that in the lower jaw there are three incisors, one canine,

The male (right) and female that I observed during their early June courtship. The male ate sparingly and seemed content to follow the female wherever she might lead.

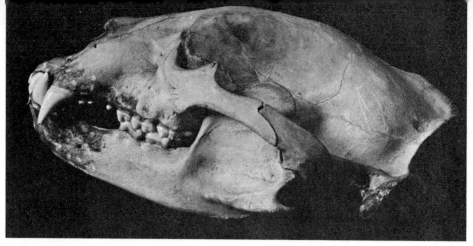

The skull of a mature black bear. Note the missing premolars and the way the crushing surfaces of the molars meet.

four premolars, and three molars on each side. The upper jaw is the same except that it has only two molars on each side.

With its incisors a bear can, when in the mood, nip at things most delicately, such as it occasionally does when it wants to pick berries only, without leaves or twigs. The canine teeth are large, long, and pointed. Coupled with strong jaws they are most formidable weapons.

The most striking difference between the teeth of a black bear and those of other carnivores is in the molars. With the swing to an omnivorous diet, over many thousands of years the ursine molars have gradually evolved into low, flat-crowned teeth. They are of the crushing type rather than the cutting type. Bears have no carnassial, or flesh-cutting, teeth such as bobcats, coyotes, and cougars have. In this respect they are like other omnivores—pigs and men, for example.

When bears finally leave their dens in the spring, they do not return to them until it is again time for their winter sleep. During their waking period they establish no permanent home but instead lead a nomadic existence within a limited range. Solitary mature males may have a home range of some fifteen miles' radius. Smaller bears and females with cubs confine themselves to an area believed to have about a ten-mile radius—about 300 square miles.

The size of a bear's home territory is thought to be less in California

88

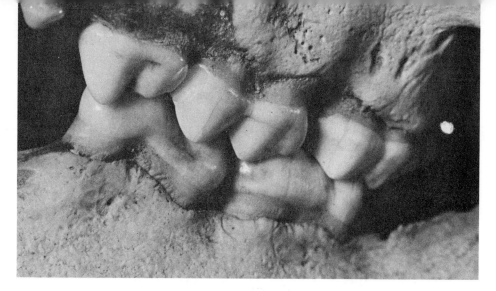

The molars of a black bear are built for crushing and grinding.

and Maine, possibly of only five miles' radius, or around 78 square miles. Recent studies in Michigan, reported by Albert W. Erickson and his associates, indicate somewhat smaller ranges than described above. In any event, black bears show no migratory tendencies except on those rare occasions when grizzlies invade their territories. Then they usually leave rather than attempt to defend their home range against this larger, stronger invader.

In the record of the Lewis and Clark Expedition, covering the explorations from May 14, 1804, to September 24, 1806, there is no report of the sighting or killing of any black bears in the area from western North Dakota to the Bitterroot Mountains in western Montana. Yet in this same area they saw a great many grizzly bears. Whether this was because the habitat was unsuitable for black bears or the grizzlies had driven them out can only be surmised. However, the aggressiveness of the grizzlies and the large number of them in the area, as indicated by the expedition reports, tends to support a theory that life might have been quite hazardous for any black bears there.

Black bears show no great "home country" instinct. If a given range provides adequate food and shelter they seem to adopt it readily. A Michigan study disclosed that transplanted bears mostly re-establish themselves in the new area. Two showed an amazing homing instinct,

89

however. One returned 96 miles and another 64 miles to their original range.

It seems likely that before the black bear was hunted and harassed by man it moved about as much by day as by night. But man changed all that. Now wild bears are seldom seen during daylight unless they have been disturbed or their appetites have urged them to start feeding early.

This does not apply, of course, to the bears in some of our national parks. Although they still do considerable night wandering, as over-turned garbage cans and the wreckage of inadequately protected tourist food supplies will attest, it is probable that most of these park bears —with the possible exception of Yellowstone's grizzlies—are as active during the day as at night. For this is when the tourists are on hand with their illegal food handouts and garbage trucks bring fresh supplies to the refuse pits.

When traveling through their home territories, bears follow well-worn trails that may have been in existence for many generations of bears. Almost always these trails are testimony to some bear's instinctive engineering ability, since they are generally the best routes to travel through the area.

Once a bear trail has been established, all traveling bears seem to follow it and even step in the footprints of their predecessors. In one reported case, where the ground was soft, this practice resulted in a series of alternating depressions as deep as twelve inches.

Black bears meander about within their home range feeding as they go. They generally spend the day bedded down in timber thickets located in a strategic spot from which they can slip away quietly if they are disturbed. One such bed discovered in Yosemite Valley had been dug in loamy soil at the base of a large pine tree. It was located in front of a huge talus slope and screened by a manzanita bush. The bear was thus provided with a secluded bed positioned so that anyone coming up from below could be seen. The bed measured 36 inches by 30 inches and was 14 inches deep.

A bear generally beds down in the same thicket in its own neighborhood, but it may not necessarily use the same bed. Ordinarily there is only one bear to a thicket at a time unless a female is with her cubs.

A bear's travels are governed to a great extent by the food supply. When there is an abundance, such as huckleberries on a hillside, the animal may stay around and use the same nest more than once. On occasion several bears may be found in such areas of plenty but it is the food rather than the company that is the attraction. Bears are not gregarious by nature.

Females with cubs do not generally travel as far or as fast as bears unencumbered with offspring and must, also, exercise greater care in the choice of a bedding site. Ground locations are more comfortable but the mother sometimes chooses a tree for herself and cubs. She may weigh around 200 pounds but is able to relax while sprawled lengthwise on a limb as small as 4 inches in diameter. She hangs her legs down on each side and sleeps soundly and safely.

Most smaller black bears are prone to play it safe and use trees as sleeping and resting places, especially if there are larger bears in the vicinity.

Surprisingly enough, bears in the wild are seldom sick. This seems all the more unusual because of their inclination to eat all manner of garbage, rotten or otherwise, as well as carrion in advanced stages of decomposition. Some of this carrion undoubtedly comes from diseased animals. It appears that a bear does overreach his digestive capabilities at times, but apparently suffers from nothing worse than a bear-sized bellyache which eventually takes care of itself naturally.

Except in early spring, when food is somewhat scarce, most bears appear fat and healthy. I have observed an occasional bear, usually one that appears to be two or three years old, with more of a "race horse" build than mature animals. But I'm inclined to think this is due more to their youth and the active life they lead staying out of the way of the larger bears than to disease or malnutrition. I can recall seeing only one bear that seemed to be in ill health.

This is the only black bear I have ever seen that seemed to be in poor health.

Twenty-five species of parasites are known to infect black bears. Ectoparasites include ticks, lice, and fleas but infestations seem to be quite rare. Endoparasites commonly in black bears are trichinae, ascarids, the microfilariids. Others, not so common, include roundworms, tapeworms, lungworms, eyeworms, hookworms, and flukes.

Diseases that have been reported in black bears are tuberculosis, anthrax, liposarcoma tumors of the uterine horns, tumors on the eyelid and scrotum, and bronchopneumonia.

Skeletal disorders appear occasionally and are caused, apparently, by injuries received in fighting or by man (bullet wounds, for example). Fortunately, black bears possess an amazing ability to recover. They withstand infection well, fractured bones mend readily, and they display a remarkable inclination to survive amputations.

92

Summer

Dental troubles are fairly common in older black bears. Individuals in their prime are less afflicted with tooth problems and young and immature bears have almost none. In older bears, canines are frequently broken and teeth may be dark and appear stained. Tooth decay is only a minor hazard. Most of a bear's dental troubles come from injuries to a single tooth which can lead to infection.

A mature black bear has very few enemies. His worst enemy is man. In fact, man can easily wipe out a bear population except, possibly, in extremely formidable terrain. Cougars, grizzlies, the big brown bears of Alaska, and wolves are also acknowledged enemies of the black bear. Two of these could be considered doubtful. A cougar would surely think a long time before attacking a mature healthy black bear, and wolves would probably only be dangerous in a pack.

Bobcats and black bear share a common range in many areas, but there seems to be no conflict between the species.

A shy resident of some black bear range is the Marten, Martes americana. *These small weasel-like mammals are much too agile to be caught by black bear.*

There are other animals capable of doing considerable damage to bears, but they cannot properly be classified as enemies because they fight only in defense and do not ordinarily attack a bear. This group includes moose and elk. A bull moose is a big and powerful animal, and it is likely that with hoof blows it could beat off, and even kill, a black bear. The massive antlered bull elk could surely do irreparable damage to any black bear foolish enough to get in its way.

Oddly enough, the comparatively small porcupine does the most damage to black bears. A skilled and careful bear can kill and eat a porcupine in safety but if it is a little careless it will get a mouthful of quills. Incidents are known wherein a black bear passing near a porcupine has given the animal a sweeping pat with one paw. This ill-considered blow may have been just another example of a black bear's innate playfulness, but with the pain from a paw full of quills, all playfulness vanishes. The angry bear may snap viciously at the porcupine.

94

Although elk calves may occasionally fall prey to a black bear that stumbles on to their hiding places, the mighty bulls with their massive antlers are in no danger.

This is the bear's second mistake and quite possibly his last. A mouth and tongue full of quills often brings slow death by starvation.

M. P. Skinner, in writing of bears in Yellowstone National Park, describes how one of his saddle horses, a gelding, would attack bears on sight. His horse had killed two black bears with lightning quick blows from his hind hooves.

It is quite likely that a black bear is its own worst enemy. It is deathly afraid of grizzlies and will avoid contact with them whenever possible. However, this is not the case with members of its own kind. While black bears are basically loners, they will fight over mates, food, cubs, or some minor matter. Occasionally, the fights result in death.

Forest fires are a considerable menace to the well-being of black

95

Mule deer are found in much of the black bear's western range.

bear. They are thought to be too intelligent to be trapped and burned by the actual flames, but the fire destroys the habitat they know and forces them into unknown areas which may not be well suited to their welfare and survival.

Earlier I described two fights between mature black bears which I had been fortunate enough to witness. Fights between such great wild beasts are most impressive, partly, I believe, because they often result in death. Any battle where the stakes are that high is impressive. However, what I remember most vividly about these encounters is the amount of noise the battlers made.

I had heard a lot of noise before from cubs, yearlings, and mature bears, but I was not prepared for the mad bull-like bellowings of rage that filled the forest. I do not know if all other sounds in the area ceased; maybe it just seemed that way. One thing appears certain, however. The other bears in the vicinity were as impressed as I, and re-

96

sponded by running away or climbing a convenient tree. I suspect that other residents of the forest, the deer, squirrels, and birds, paid heed to the sound and either left the area or hunted for a place of safety.

Black bears have a great range of vocal abilities, possibly more than most mammals. However, they seem to do most of their "talking" when around other bears, and since the mature animals are loners, they don't get much chance for conversation.

Apparently, the cubs start making noises almost as soon as they are born. J. R. Matson, who kept a denned female with cubs under close observation for three and one-half months, reported sounds on January 4. He thought the cubs were less than a day old at the time and described the sounds as follows: "I could hear squeaks, like little pigs."

William H. Wright, who spent a lot of time in bear country in the early 1900's, stated that he had heard newborn cubs whimpering inside the den many times.

After they leave the den, a mother and cubs use a language of grunts, mumbles, coughs, squeaks, whines, and whimpers. They seem to have little difficulty in understanding one another. The right grunt sends a cub scurrying up the nearest tree. Similarly, a howl of fright or a bawl of pain from the cubs will bring the mother bear on the run. If separated from the mother for very long, cubs will cry for hours in a whimpering, high-pitched moan, that rises and falls.

An angry bear snarls and growls and roars with rage. When threatened it may give a low warning growl accompanied by threats expressed by champing its jaws and clicking its teeth together. A startled bear may snort or make a whistling sound by expelling its breath suddenly and violently. This "whooshing" sound is also used to bluff unwelcome intruders.

Some years ago I was photographing a benign-looking black bear that was lying on the shoulder of the road near West Thumb in Yellowstone National Park. This was in early October and the bear, an old male, was probably ill-tempered from a summer's exposure to tour-

97

A moment after this picture was made this sleepy looking old black bear jumped at me with a great whoosh!

ists. I was working from the safety of the car at a distance of 8 feet and was focusing on the calm, peaceful expression on the bear's face as seen closeup through a 150-mm. telephoto lens. Suddenly the image blurred and with a great whoosh the bear jumped straight at me. My reactions were much faster than I realized and without quite knowing just how I got there, I was a hundred yards down the road. Then I stopped the car and had a good, although somewhat nervous, laugh at myself.

I am convinced the old bear was just bluffing. All he wanted was to be let alone. I might add that it was a good bluff that worked. I left the old boy to enjoy himself quietly in the warm autumn sunshine.

A bear in pain will bawl and sob like a human. A man whose bear hunting ended after one day described to me how a big male he had shot in the chest stood with his two forepaws clasped over the wound crying and moaning like a person. The experience unnerved him so that he never hunted bears again.

Paintings often show a giant black bear casually flipping fish out of a fast, white-water stream—sometimes to a pair of waiting cubs. The inspiration for these pictures was likely the big brown bears of Alaska that feed extensively on salmon on their way upstream to spawn. It is probably from such pictures that many people get the idea that the black bear is a great fisherman and that fish form a substantial part of its diet. Both ideas are incorrect. If a black bear catches a fish it is probably a near-dead spawner or, more likely, one already dead.

That black bears are often seen near streams and swimming in lakes might also appear to support the bear-as-a-fisherman theory, but in reality the bear is there simply because it likes water. As a matter of fact, water is essential to the well-being of a bear and it drinks considerable quantities. Normally, it goes to the watering places once a day, but during periods of heavy feeding it makes the trip twice a day.

Water contributes greatly to the bears' comfort during hot weather. Black bears are reported to have regular bathing holes, and they swim readily, sometimes as much as five miles at a time. They have one odd habit which can be dangerous not only for the bears but to anything in their path—they swim in a straight line and will not change direction no matter what might be in the way. They will go over anything—man, rock, log, or moose; when they get to shore they climb up and over whatever is there rather than move a few feet to the side where a landing would be much easier. Indians are reported to have taken advantage of this peculiarity by standing knee deep in water alongside a swimming bear's right-of-way and killing it with a tomahawk.

99

The dried mud on this old bear's rump indicates it had recently visited a wallow.

Black bears especially like a muddy pool where they can retreat during the hot midday periods and lie and wallow in the mud for ten minutes or so. When they leave a pool they do not shake off the surplus water in the manner of a dog but allow it to remain in their fur and prolong the cooling effect as much as possible. Mosquitoes and other insects are quite bothersome to a bear during parts of the summer, and muddy wallows and swims in lakes or streams afford the animal some relief. This same activity also assists shedding of the old fur.

Observations indicate that young cubs do not take to their mud baths quite as readily as their mothers. However, they have been seen swimming on extremely warm days. It is likely that the youngsters do not suffer from excessive heat as much as the older bears, and they would not, of course, be bothered with the itching from the shedding of heavy winter fur. One observer reported seeing more bears at wallows in the fall than at any other season.

Through the long warm days of summer the cubs have been growing and learning. The mother bear has introduced them to all manner of natural foods and has shown them how to dig for insects and roots and where to find the choicest berries. In the process the young bears sample the food and find it good. They then spend less time at their

100

mother's teats and more time eating grasshoppers and mice and grass. By August or September they are usually weaned. However, they do not leave the mother at this time.

Autumn

DURING THE SPRING and summer months black bear cubs are transformed from tiny awkward babies into clever, agile juveniles. Larger bears go from fat to thin, and back to fat again; their fur from smooth and glossy to ragged and dull, and then back to smooth and glossy. All this happens so naturally that we are more or less unaware of the changes. It is like our seasons—winter, spring, and summer. Their approach is subtle, and one season fades into another with no definite beginning or end.

However, this is not true of autumn. We go to bed one night and it is still summer. We wake up to a frost-whitened morning. Fall has arrived. Aspen leaves turn a brilliant gold almost overnight, and tiny green ground shrubs change to an unbelievable red. This dramatic change in nature's coloring seems to be reflected in equally dramatic changes in animals.

Overnight, it seems, the buck deer loses the velvet covering of his antlers. He walks the shadowed forests, his head high, while the polished rapierlike points of his antlers proclaim his new status. The first flights of southbound geese appear overhead. Their wild music drifts down and grows fainter as they follow ancient migration routes. Patches of snow-matching white appear in the fur of the varying hare.

And so, it seems, black bears are suddenly fat and contented, their coats thick and glossy. The cubs which were so tiny when they first appeared in the spring now look half as big as their mothers (though they are not).

102

Autumn

Like most other mammals, the sleek-coated black bear occasionally finds an unexpected blond mixed in with the normal black, brown, and cinnamon-colored specimens. These are albinos or part albinos. They are extremely rare, of course, but Ernest Thompson Seton mentions two cases among eastern black bears. In another recorded instance, a white female had four cubs—an unusual happening in itself. Included in the litter was one brown cub and two black ones, but the fourth was a true albino. Both the mother and the albino cub had red eyes and toenails, and the skin of their lips was black.

In 1948 a black bear killed in Wyoming's Shoshone National Forest was a brown color phase and had a white breast and white front feet. This animal was probably a partial albino.

Almost the reverse coloring was reported in June, 1964, by a U. S.

Most of the time a black bear moves along with a slow shuffling gait.

The World of the Black Bear

Forest Service biologist and his pilot who were flying up the South Fork of the Walla Walla River in northeastern Oregon. There is nothing unusual about seeing bears in this part of the state, but when they spotted one that was light colored they went in for a closer look. They reported a full grown black bear, with its head and feet a light chocolate color but the rest of the body a dirty white.

Melanism, an excess of black pigmentation, is apparently unknown in the species or, for obvious reasons, undetectable.

Most of the time a black bear ambles slowly along with a shuffling gait, its head low and swinging from side to side. It will stop and claw at a rotten log that might house grubs or other insects, or graze for a few minutes on some desirable vegetation. It may even pause for a slow luxurious rub against the rough bark of a convenient tree. Something unusual along the way will attract the bear into a leisurely side trip to satisfy its naturally strong curiosity.

Most of these movements are made at an unhurried two- or three-mile-an-hour pace, which seems to be the normal speed of an undisturbed black bear. They eat more or less continuously all day long and are probably never ravenous, except possibly in the early spring. Consequently, there is generally nothing to rush a bear. Since he sleeps wherever and whenever he chooses and can find something to eat almost anywhere, there is never much reason for him to hurry—except when he's frightened.

When this happens, the animal leaps into action at once and loses no time in trying to determine whether the danger is real or fancied. The contrast between a black bear running at top speed and the leisurely walk most often associated with the animal is so great that one imagines it is going much faster than it really is.

Most estimates of a bear's top running speed are around 25 miles per hour. John Evic Hill described how a large black bear ran in front of the headlights of a vehicle for several hundred yards. Its speed as measured by the speedometer never exceeded 30 miles per hour. This

The normal slow walk of a black bear is misleading for when the need arises they can move out rapidly as this yearling, threatened by a larger bear, is doing.

is fast for an animal the size and shape of a black bear and is probably fast enough to give it the potential to be a killer of game. But it seems that when a bear does try for a deer or some other animal, either wild or domestic, it hunts from ambush and relies on surprise rather than speed.

Black bears have some awkward-looking movements between their slow and fast speeds. I have seen them bounce along in a sort of fast walk, and I am always reminded of an elephant trying to run. When these animals really get going it is quite a spectacle. The long hind legs reach farther and farther forward and outside at every jump so that the back arches until the animal looks like a speeding ball. They jump over rocks and logs in their path, dodge around trees, and plow right through any clumps of bushes that get in their way.

I watched a frightened black bear going through some manzanita brush in the Cascades of central Oregon at full speed, and the brush didn't seem to slow it down a bit. This is tough, wiry brush that grows

105

The World of the Black Bear

thick and, in some places, head high. I have tried to force my way through it a time or two without much success.

A friend of mine watched a bear racing at full speed through the mountainous timbered section of northeastern Oregon. He and a companion had watched it run for a couple of hundred yards when another member of their party spotted the fleeing animal and started shooting at it. This urging kept the bear moving at top speed, and they estimated that it ran for a distance of two miles before they lost sight of it. While they had no way to determine speed, they thought it was going about 30 miles an hour.

Despite the bear's awkward appearance at times, it is one of the most sure-footed mammals in the forest. This is undoubtedly a great help when it is running through the woods at breakneck speed.

The clumsy-looking shuffling gait of the black bear is due in part to the kind of feet the animal has—and accounts for its designation as a

A black bear walks flat-footed with its heels touching the ground.

plantigrade animal. This means it walks flat-footed with its heels touching the ground. Raccoons, badgers, porcupines, and beavers—along with man—are plantigrade animals.

Cats and dogs are examples of digitigrade animals that stand on their toes and whose heels do not touch the ground. They can generally move more quickly than plantigrade animals. Deer and goats are unguligrades; they stand on the tips of their toenails and are usually faster than either of the other two classes.

A black bear's feet are large, broad, five-toed, and the digits are almost equal in length. The black or brown soles are naked. The non-retractile claws are strong and heavy, with an extremely arched curve, and are the same color as the fur. Naturally the claws will vary in length depending on the size of the animal and the amount of wear they have had, but they seldom exceed 1½ inches. Mature grizzlies and big brown bears rarely have claws less than 1¾ inches long.

The amazing strength inherent in a black bear's claws is indicated in this story I heard from a friend several years ago. He was telling of a late spring bear hunt in the big fir timber country on the western slope of the Cascade Range a few miles north of the town of Oakridge, Oregon. This is rough mountainous country along the North Fork of the Willamette River. The pack of hounds took the trail of a large male black bear about nine in the morning. Baying lustily, the pack followed the trail at a fast clip down a canyon and up the other side. The hunters were trying to follow the hounds on foot, but the rough terrain made it difficult. They heard the baying of the trailing hounds change to a frantic bawling when the pack jumped the bear. Then, apparently, the bear and dogs went over another ridge and could no longer be heard. For several hours the hunters moved about the area, stopping at strategic listening posts. Finally, about three in the afternoon, they heard the faint sound of the hounds baying "treed."

Fifteen minutes later they came upon the pack ringing a fir tree three feet in diameter where a large black bear was clinging like a

The feet of a black bear, hind foot at left, front feet at right. The claws are strong and heavy and have a strongly arched curve.

The feet of a Great Brown bear. The claws are longer than those of a black bear, but mature specimens are unable to climb trees.

The hind-foot print of a black bear.

squirrel to the trunk some thirty feet up. It was supporting its weight, which they estimated to be 250 to 300 pounds, with its claws. The nearest limb was a long way above the animal, and there were no claw marks in the bark to indicate that it had been higher.

Judging from the length of time the dogs had been lost and the comparatively short distance the bear had apparently traveled, this animal had been clinging to the tree supported only by its claws for three to five hours.

A bear's forepaw is short and its tracks look as if only the toes and ball of the foot touch the ground. The long rear foot makes a definite heel print and its tracks look like those of a large man wearing moccasins. The imprints of all five toes both front and back show clearly in a

109

The World of the Black Bear

black bear's tracks, but only rarely can one see the claw imprints. The size of black bear footprints will naturally vary. A medium-sized California black bear made hind foot tracks measuring 8 inches long and 5 inches wide. The front foot track was 4 inches long and 5 inches wide. However, there are records of tracks considerably larger—10½ inches long and 7 inches wide, for example. A bear just ambling along will stride about 12 inches, and in so doing make a double row of tracks, one on each side of a given center line. A bear walks by moving alternate feet on alternate sides. That is, he starts on the right forefoot and follows with the left hind foot. Now the left forefoot and then the

A bear walks with alternate feet on alternate sides. This one has placed his right forefoot down and the left hind foot is about to touch. Then the left forefoot will reach out (it has already started), and the right hind foot will follow.

right hind foot move forward. The hind foot comes down about $3\frac{1}{2}$ inches in front of the impression left by the forefoot on the same side.

In addition to their footprints, black bears leave other evidence of their presence and passage. While feeding they will turn over rocks and tear old stumps to pieces. Fruit trees broken when an apple hungry bear has put too much of his weight on a limb and torn up berry patches are bear signs. Also the droppings of the animal are always present in bear country. These often contain large amounts of grasses, root fibers, beetle casings, ants, fruit seeds, berries, and nut shells, suggesting what the diet of the animal is.

Bear nests and wallows are reliable signs but are not frequently seen, partly because the scooped-out nests are often in thickets or other locations not easily visible and wallows may not be too plentiful.

Probably the most controversial of all bear signs is the "bear tree." For no apparent reason a black bear traveling the familiar trails on its range will select a tree and, while standing erect on its hind legs, make several claw and tooth marks at what appears to be its maximum reach. A bear may also stand with its back to the tree and stretch upward, running its nose, head, neck, and back against the tree. Thus hair, mud, and a vast amount of scent will cling to the bark.

No particular tree gets preferential treatment from black bears, although aspen are mentioned most often, possibly because scratches show clearly on the white trunk of this species. Bear marks have been observed on yellow birch, white birch, aspen, balsam fir, white cedar, and others. Bears don't always select a tree to scratch and bite. Some years ago, in a thickly timbered section on the eastern slope of the central Oregon Cascades, bears clawed and chewed the post and sign of a U. S. Forest Service trail marker so much that it finally fell apart.

It has been contended that only males mark trees and that the height of the claw marks is an indication of the size, strength, and ferocity of the bear making them. Thus, the trees represent a warning to all other bears, or, at least, to all other bears of less stature, to stay out

111

A tree with bear scratches in Crater Lake National Park.

of the territory. This theory is unsatisfactory because females have been observed marking trees in this manner and bear scratches have been seen in the tops of trees.

Another explanation of claw marks is that the bear in all probability was merely cleaning or sharpening its claws by scratching them on something solid, in the manner of a house cat. This interpretation, of course, has the virtue of being simple, but I am inclined to think the answer is more complex.

It seems reasonable to assume that a "bear tree" serves the same purpose as the "scent post" or urinary post of the coyote. With its sensitive nose, a black bear can undoubtedly obtain a great deal of information about previous visitors to a bear tree. We can only guess at what a thorough investigation of such a tree reveals to a black bear, but it surely indicates whether or not there has been a recent visitor. The sex of each animal is possibly a part of the message left, and it may be that bears can recognize the scent of friends or enemies.

112

Autumn

It does not seem that scratching the tree would be necessary if a bear wanted only to leave identifying scent around. It could be that it stretches and claws the tree trunk simply because some predecessor did the same, therefore showing it was a good tree for the purpose. I have been unable to find any reference to unclawed bear trees, which, naturally, would not be noticeable, but I do not believe we should rule out the possibility of the existence of "bear trees" that are not also claw-sharpening trees. For example, I have seen the same tree used for back-scratching purposes by several bears. But whether this was some type of "bear tree" or whether it was just an accident that various bears found it a suitable scratching post I had no way of determining.

When a cub comes out of the den in early spring it weighs approximately 5 pounds and follows its mother around with considerable difficulty. By July 1, average weight may be up to 24 pounds. At this time, the cubs are playful youngsters that move easily and climb rapidly with great skill. Already they have begun to supplement their diet of milk with bits of a variety of natural foods brought to their attention by the mother bear.

A six-month-old cub searching for natural food, even though it is probably still getting most of its nourishment from its mother's milk.

The World of the Black Bear

Their first permanent teeth begin breaking through in June. About the time they retire for their first winter's sleep all their permanent teeth will be in except the canines. These may have just started through, but they will continue to grow during the dormancy period and be ready for use when the bears emerge the following spring.

Cubs continue to gain weight throughout the fall at a slightly accelerated rate and at ten months, or around December 1, will weigh from 30 to 80 pounds, or an average of 55 pounds. In November, three bear cubs raised in captivity weighed 86, 59, and 62½ pounds respectively, but these greater than average weights could have been due to the food available to them as compared with that available to wild bears and to the fact that they didn't have to work very hard for it. Also, weights seem to vary in different parts of the country. Howard E. Spencer, Jr., reports: "It appears that Maine cubs may reach a weight of 45 to 95 pounds . . . by November or December."

A Pennsylvania growth study showed twenty-two-month-old bears to

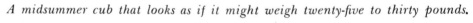

A midsummer cub that looks as if it might weigh twenty-five to thirty pounds.

weigh between 80 and 130 pounds and average 105; thirty-four-month-old bears from 215 to 295 and average 255; and seventy-month-old bears weigh between 255 and 350 pounds and average 305.

Cubs lose their baby fur during the summer months and immediately start growing a coat more suitable for the cold winter ahead. M. P. Skinner states: "In the same way, cubs, when they lose their baby fur, may become darker during the first autumn and even change from brown to black. I have even known yearling bears to change from brown to black at the annual shedding time."

By the time the cubs are ready to follow their mother into the den for their first winter's sleep, they are fat and round and sleek in their long heavy coats that will keep them warm even on the coldest winter night.

Despite the fact that cubs usually stay with their mother until they are fifteen to sixteen months old, they can be self-sufficient when they are as young as 5½ months and as small as 18 pounds. Even on unfamiliar range and handicapped by physical injury, they seem to get along remarkably well.

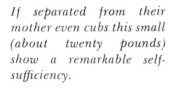

If separated from their mother even cubs this small (about twenty pounds) show a remarkable self-sufficiency.

115

The black bear's fondness for rugged, remote timbered areas, along with its cautious nature, has enabled the species to survive over much of the same range as in pre-pioneer times.

Back in the days when Indians had this country all to themselves, areas now devoted to cities and farm lands were still covered with heavy stands of virgin timber. There were probably enough black bears around then so that any Indian brave needing a new bearskin robe could take to the woods with bow and arrow or spear, and by the use of his hunting skills dispatch one within a reasonable length of time.

As the American pioneer settled in the East and began to open up the country, he cleared away the brush and timber so vital to the welfare of the black bear. With his rifle the pioneer protected his family, killing bears when they were a threat, or as a source of food. Their fat, meat and hides were all useful.

With the disappearance of much of its protective cover in this country, the black bear has retreated into the rugged, remote timbered

116

areas that remain. It is wary and scary and would rather run than fight. This is not because the animal lacks courage, if we can properly use that term in relation to a wild animal, but simply because it, like most wild animals, fights only when survival is at stake. This characteristic plus the capacity to eat and exist on almost anything has been a major factor in its survival.

The black bear, generally, has an undeserved bad reputation in this country. Many Americans consider it a veritable monster. It is quite possible that some of the grizzly's deserved reputation for ferocity has rubbed off on the black bear. I am sure that most bear hunters embellish their stories with more or less fictional incidents or, at the very least, a certain amount of exaggeration. Of course, black bears can become extremely dangerous when cornered, harassed by a pack of hounds, or wounded.

However, the bear hunts I've had anything to do with and the stories told to me by several men who have hunted bear most of their lives suggest that unless a person does something extremely foolish, danger is negligible when hunting black bears.

Most bears are killed incidentally, when the hunters are actually after deer, elk, or moose. This probably happens most often when a bear frightened by the scent or noise of one hunter starts moving away and thus exposes itself to the others. Unfortunately, most hunters shoot at bears, even those encountered accidentally. I have met people who killed bears while deer or elk hunting; they always seem to be quite proud of themselves, though I don't understand why. Seldom does a hunting season go by without a newspaper story about a man who killed three bears while out deer hunting. The picture accompanying the story generally shows the brave hunter standing next to the bodies of a female black bear and her two 50-pound cubs hanging from a tree.

Luck rather than skill is the most important ingredient in this kind of bear hunting.

Most successful planned bear hunting is done with especially trained

117

hound packs. Methods will vary somewhat in different parts of the country according to the terrain and cover in which the bear is being hunted. E. V. Richards, describing bear hunting in Virginia, says that as many as fifty hunters and fifty dogs may go on a bear hunt. "Hunters take up 'stands' along trails, ridges, hollows or any well-known crossing. . . . The bear may be treed by the dogs or decide to make a stand and fight. Most bears are driven past a 'bear stand' and are shot by the waiting hunter."

This kind of bear hunting seems to be more attractive to "hound men" than ordinary hunters. In many backwoods communities of the East men are known by the quality of their bear dogs, but I have also known men in the Northwest who were proud of their hunting dogs. In talking to these men I have come to the conclusion that the killing of the bear, or cougar, or bobcat—all of which are hunted mostly with hounds—is incidental to the real purpose of the hunt, which is to have the dogs work well. These hunters seem to feel that they must bring in the game as tangible proof of the capabilities of their dogs.

There is obviously little skill or sport involved in shooting a bear seated in a tree a few feet away. Nor is it a feat when the animal makes a stand on the ground. However, the latter position might be rough on the dogs and could be dangerous to a hunter who goes in close to protect his pack.

In some areas baits are used to attract bears. I have heard of hunters placing dead domestic animals at strategic places in bear country and then visiting them at intervals. When a bear discovers a bait of this size he cannot consume it quickly, and the hunters know he will stay in the vicinity. Once they get a bear interested in a bait, it is a simple matter to put the dogs on the trail for a hunt that is usually both short and successful.

In a recent article in one of the popular outdoor magazines, the author reported limited success in luring black bears within gun range

118

with a predator call. Much has been written in recent years about calling coyotes, bobcats, and foxes, but this is the only report of calling black bears that I have found. The author expressed the opinion that curiosity rather than an expected meal caused the bear to come in to investigate.

A .30-30 rifle is generally considered adequate for black bear hunting. Larger calibers, of course, will also serve the purpose. Shotguns loaded with buckshot are frequently used in the southeastern United States. However, small caliber rifles, such as standard .22 rimfire, are inadequate and dangerous. They will most often merely wound and irritate a bear. The animal, in pain from its wound, can be extremely dangerous.

A young man I met several years ago told me of getting mixed up with a big black bear while armed only with a .22 rimfire automatic pistol. He would not have attempted to shoot the animal with such an inadequate weapon except that the bear was about to kill one of his dogs. He tried several shots at the bear's head but that only made it mad. The bear left the dogs and started after the young man, who turned and ran. However, the dogs kept nipping at the bear's unprotected rear so that it then abandoned its pursuit of the hunter. Unable to penetrate the bear's skull with the light .22-caliber bullets, the man changed his target to the animal's neck. He exhausted his ammunition supply but finally killed the bear, having fired a total of nine shots at 10- and 20-foot distances.

Most states now consider the black bear a game animal and have established seasons and require licenses to hunt them. A few states, however, still have no closed season on bears. The use of dogs in bear hunting has been outlawed in a few areas, but inasmuch as any kind of hunting success is doubtful without dogs, it seems unlikely that this restriction will be adopted in most of the states with large bear populations for some time yet.

119

However, many of the eastern states have established much-needed restrictions on the killing of cubs. In general, these protect a cub during its first year only.

Bear hunting will undoubtedly continue to be an activity limited to a relatively few participants, especially when compared to the millions who annually take to the woods to hunt deer. I was unable to obtain any report acceptable as accurate of the number of black bears killed annually by hunters. My own estimate, based on the information I was able to obtain, is between 15,000 and 20,000 animals. This includes those killed in Alaska.

Bear trapping has been, and still is, used mostly to control stock-killing bears and, in the Northwest, to control bears damaging the tree farms of the area. Also, in central Oregon there are a few people who trap bears primarily for food. While steel traps are most common, steel snares are sometimes used.

The steel traps are necessarily large ones and are usually set in a pen devised of logs built in the shape of a V. The bait is placed in the closed end of the pen and the trap set in the center of the open end. Logs or stones are usually placed across the open end in such a manner as to encourage a bear after the bait to step into the trap. Since these bear traps are so large and strong they are extremely dangerous to man. Setting one requires great skill and care. For safety's sake two men often handle the chore. Caution must also be exercised to prevent casual woods travelers, such as hikers or fishermen, from getting caught. One way this is done is to place a log across the top of the open end of the V low enough to keep a man from going in but high enough for the bear to get under. Warning signs around the trap are also used.

Bait for traps often consists of the remains of bear-killed livestock. Singed flesh combined with honey or fruit is also recommended. Trappers in the predator control branch of the U. S. Fish and Wildlife Service in Oregon find the heads of slaughtered cattle a good bait. The heads are generally split open for the purpose.

120

Autumn

Bear traps are fastened to a drag so that the bear can move away, at a slow pace. If the trap were fastened to a tree or some other immovable object, the bear might tear loose. A green hardwood pole 5 inches in diameter at the small end and 7 or 8 feet long is recommended by one expert.

Bearskins have little commercial value as fur. They are most highly prized as hunting trophies, either as rugs or wall hangings. The fur becomes prime late, usually just before the winter sleep period. It is still prime when the bear comes out in the spring.

Indians and early settlers slept on bearskins and also prized the skins as warm robes. They were sometimes made into winter coats. I remember, back in the days of the Model T with its open sides and no heater, when, as a five-year-old, I kept warm on icy winter days by snuggling under a bearskin robe.

An interesting use of black bear fur in these modern times is in the impressive fur headgear worn by the Guards regiments in England. These luxurious head pieces undoubtedly add greatly to the stature and impressiveness of the guardsmen. The Quebec Guards in Canada wear a similar headgear of black bear fur.

There is a wide range of opinion about the fitness of bear meat for human consumption. Bear meat varies in palatability all the way from delicious to horrible. But then so do other wild meats. It depends almost entirely upon the individual animal. I've eaten venison that could hardly have been better and I've had some that was most foul. The same is true of pronghorn antelope. And I can well remember a fine-looking Canada goose that no amount of cooking could tenderize.

The early white settlers relied heavily upon the bear for meat as well as for fat needed for cooking and other purposes. I'm sure that they, along with those Indians whose religion did not forbid the eating of bear, knew how to get the most edible bears and probably confined their hunting to those.

A full-grown but young black bear makes the choicest eating, espe-

121

cially if it has been feeding on grains, roots, berries, and the like. Meat from an old bear is apt to be coarse, tough, and strong. If the bear has been feeding on carrion or fish, flavor will be further tainted. A bear killed after a long hot pursuit is not apt to be very good, nor is a skinny bear.

Bear meat is dark in color, and all the fat should be trimmed off before cooking. It seems to be generally agreed that roasting is the best way to cook it. However, steaks and chops may be broiled. Since bears can be carriers of the trichina worm, the meat should be thoroughly cooked to avoid trichinosis. Another highly recommended method for preparing bear meat is to smoke or cure it in the same manner as pork. Bear meat also makes good sausage. Some cooks use all sorts of seasonings and sauces along with a great deal of precooking treatment.

A bear in December, fat and ready for the winter, will yield 10 to 15 gallons of oil. Colonists used it in medicines, hair tonics, perfume, and as an olive oil substitute. It was also considered a cure for various ailments such as rheumatism and sprains.

Bear grease, or oil, rendered from the fat of black bears, was one of the mainstays of the pioneer. In fact, it appears to have been the "miracle drug" of its day. In an article in *Virginia Wildlife* Eddie W. Wilson notes: "In 1682, Thomas Ashe, while advertising the real estate of the Lord Proprietors in Carolina to his English countrymen, said: 'Bears there are in great number of whose fat they make an Oyl which is of great Virtue and Efficacy in causing the Hair to grow, which I observed the Indians daily used, by which means they not only keep their Hair clear and preserved from Vermine but by the nourishing faculty of the Oyl, it usually extended in length to their middles.' "

Another Englishman of about the same period told of being entertained by Indians who rubbed his eyes and joints with bear's "Oyl."

Even though bear grease may not be the longed-for cure for baldness and other infirmities, it is generally agreed that it makes an excellent cooking oil. It is said to be much better than lard for frying purposes,

122

and Palmer, along with several other reporters, has recommended it highly for cooking doughnuts. It can be used for waterproofing shoes and boots, but it will soak right through the leather and is therefore not especially desirable for this purpose.

Horace Kephart, in his classic book on camping and woodcraft, states: "Bear's oil, by the way, is better than lard for shortening biscuit and for frying, and, when mixed with sugar and spread on bread, is not a bad substitute for butter and sirup. . . . Bear's oil is superior to olive oil for the table, and can be used with impunity by people whose stomachs will not endure pork fat."

Winter

DURING THE FALL MONTHS the black bear's feeding takes on an added urgency, for in a two- or three-month period it must accumulate a sufficient supply of fat to carry it through the coming winter's period of food scarcity. By late November or early December, when a bear is ready for its winter sleep, it will have a good 3 inches of thick warm fur with a 4-inch layer of fat underneath to sustain it and keep it warm during the coming dormant period.

This winter sleep is a strange and interesting way for these animals to get through what might otherwise be a most difficult period. Furthermore, it appears to be an eminently practical way to spend the winter. Winter sleeps and periods of hibernation make it possible for some animals to exist and even expand their range in areas where it would otherwise be impossible.

It is common practice to speak of bears as hibernating, but a more accurate description is a "deep sleep." It is not true hibernation. The animal's temperature and heart beat remain substantially normal, and its breathing rate stays at four to five complete respirations a minute. Raccoons, skunks, and badgers have a similar period of winter sleep.

During true hibernation, such as that experienced by woodchucks and ground squirrels, respiration and circulation are barely perceptible, and body temperature approximates that of the surrounding air. Hibernating animals feel cold to the touch and can be handled without awakening.

Should a bear truly hibernate and its body temperature approach that of its environment, near or below freezing in many instances, the animal would be completely helpless. The female could not, under such circumstances, perform the functions required to bring forth young, such as cutting the umbilical cord, or licking life into a newly born cub.

Why a black bear goes into a long winter's sleep has been the subject of much controversy for some time. For a number of years the most widely accepted theory was that climatic temperatures were the determining factor. In other words, a bear slept through the winter to escape the cold. However, this reason has now been generally discarded. Ralph S. Palmer describes how some bears build their beds for winter sleep in locations wholly exposed to falling snow which melts on the sleeping animal.

It would certainly seem that an animal so well equipped to withstand cold weather as the black bear would not go into a winter's sleep to avoid it. William H. Wright, in his book on the black bear written in 1910, describes the winter sleep of a pet bear and says, in part: "The amount of heat that his body gave out was astonishing. I have thrust my hand under him as he slept and it actually felt hot. The steam, too, that came up through the cracks of the floor of the carriage house not only covered the carriage with frost but coated the whole inside of the room." This was in Spokane, Washington, where it is very cold during the winter months. Dormant bears have been located in Maine by observing steam issuing from the "breather hole" in the snow covering the den.

The theory that now seems to be most widely accepted is that bears sleep through the winter in order to survive a period of food scarcity. But this reasoning also has a weakness, for even in Florida the black bear sleeps for a short while when there is still plenty of food and no apparent need for a winter sleep.

Observations in California have disclosed that in certain areas of comparatively low altitude (under 3,000 feet) black bears show occa-

125

sional activity all winter long, especially in sections with warm southern exposures. This is true of bears in Mariposa County, where acorns, manzanita berries, green herbage, and similar foods are available in the winter.

Captive bears that have no period of food scarcity do not follow the same pattern of winter sleep that wild bears do. Jack Marks, superintendent of the Portland, Oregon, Zoological Gardens, tells me that the zoo's black bears may indulge in two- or three-day "cat naps," but miss very few meals during the winter months.

Since the periods of winter food scarcity vary at different latitudes, the time of beginning the winter sleep also varies. Denning in Alaska generally starts in late October. Black bears in this land of long, arduous winters may spend half their lives in dens. In Idaho and Maine the bears go into their dens in the last half of November, while in the mountain regions of California they wait until the first half of December. With the exception of females bearing young, in Mexico and southern parts of the United States black bears may not den at all, or, if they do, only for short periods.

Females and cubs take to their dens on an average of about two weeks before adult males. An adult male bear never sleeps in the same den with a female. Normally, cubs of the year, which at denning time may be from a third to half the size of their mother, will spend the winter in the same den with her or in a separate one nearby.

Marius A. Morse tells of a female and three yearlings that were found sleeping in an open black spruce swamp in northern Minnesota. The den site they had selected was on the swamp floor and its only protection came from the surrounding trees. The animals were cuddled so close together that it was difficult to determine how many bears were there. The cubs awakened and Morse could then see that their bodies were covering the head of a larger bear.

Some bears may demonstrate a restlessness all winter long and never relax into a normal winter's sleep. This seems to be related to their

126

physical condition, as a black bear's inclination to den is apparently triggered by the amount of fat it has accumulated.

When a bear begins its accelerated feeding program in the fall it eats more than it needs to meet its daily energy requirements. The balance accumulates as fat. Somewhere around the beginning of winter it reaches a saturation point. It may be so round and plump that its belly practically drags the ground. Then it loses its appetite, and its stomach shrinks until the animal appears incapable of digesting any more food.

When this happens, bears are ready for their winter sleep. It may be several days before they take to their dens, but during this period they have been known to refuse such normally desirable foods as candy.

One of the questions yet to be answered is just what causes the ending of a bear's fall feeding orgy. It apparently has not yet been determined whether a bear's stomach shrinks because it has stopped eating or it stops eating because its stomach shrinks.

However, one thing seems fairly well established—temperatures, weather conditions, and snow depth seem to have little, if anything, to do with the denning time. If satiety and obesity are the factors that determine when a bear will den, it follows that a bear with inadequate fat reserves will not retire as early as its more fortunate kin.

J. R. Matson comments: "If the accumulation is not sufficient, the activity of the bear may, and frequently does, continue during the winter."

Some authorities hold that a bear cannot hibernate unless it is fat.

There seems to be no such thing as a "typical" bear den, and the variety of sites chosen indicate surprising differences of opinion among black bears as to what constitutes an acceptable den. Females expecting cubs are among the first to go into their dens. They generally demonstrate more discrimination than males and others that den later. Possibly this is because their instincts tell them that the cubs will need more protection than adults and yearlings.

127

Russ Kinne, Photo Researchers, Inc.

A black bear in its den in Yellowstone National Park. This one has its eyes open and was probably aware of its visitors.

Pennsylvania Game Commission

A Pennsylvania black bear in its den. It was apparently oblivious to its visitors. The den is under a rocky ledge and contains some den material of leaves, etc.

Also, females and yearlings seem more inclined than adult males to provide a den lining of leaves, ferns, grasses, and similar material, but this is by no means a hard and fast rule. And while this might seem to indicate a greater concern for comfort on the part of females and yearlings, there is the possibility that it simply means that there isn't as much bedding material available to late-denning males. A den observed in New York occupied by a female and two cubs was located in a stand of small spruce trees. The mother had not prepared the site in any special manner, which indicates that some females are not too concerned about the condition of their dens.

Usually, den site selection does not seem to follow any specific requirements other than that it be sheltered, hidden, and well-drained. Sites include natural underground caves, semi-caves under rock ledges, broken rocks, hollows in large trees or in fallen logs, fallen tree trunks under drooping conifers, windfalls, thickets, or among small trees in a swamp. Sometimes a bear may dig a den in the level ground. Caves or other completely underground sites do not appear to be commonly used. In Michigan, most bears favor dens dug beneath objects such as logs or stumps, or holes dug in a hillside. When it is possible a bear may enlarge its den site by digging or merely scooping out a depression in the ground. Whether these are lined with leaves and other material seems to depend on the individual bear, but signs show that some animals spend several days preparing their dens. Often they seemingly arrange limbs and twigs to provide additional protection.

Southern exposures seem to be favored, and the location may indicate that the bear is aware of the prevailing winter winds and the need for some protection from them. Quite often the dens are so situated that snows will pile up and provide additional protection from winter's icy blasts.

An adult black bear ready to retire for the winter is a truly awesome sight. It is big and round and fat, and it would seem obvious that the

A black bear ready to retire for the winter is big and fat and round.

animal will require a large den. However, they do not need nearly as large sleeping quarters as one might think. One reported den was 2 feet deep, 4 feet wide, and 5 feet long. Another was only 34 inches square and 16 inches deep. D. F. Switzenberg describes one located in a pine tree that was 38 inches in diameter at the base and 35 inches at the opening 53 feet above the ground. The den was occupied by a bear estimated to weigh 150 pounds.

Joseph Grinnell and his associates described the den of a California black bear which was located on a brushy south-facing hillside: "This den was only a large natural crevice in a pile of gigantic boulders, surrounded by a dense growth of scrub oak, manzanita, and California laurel. The main approach was indicated by an old well-worn bear trail through the scrub oaks on the south side of the boulders. The opening

130

Winter

was merely a vertical crack leading into the center of the boulder pile. The crack, or passageway, was two feet wide, six feet high, and ten feet long. Inside, the passageway turned abruptly to the left and entered the den proper, which was 40 inches wide, 50 inches high, and 60 inches deep; the bottom was covered with a thick layer of dry dead leaves.''

A yearling used the den one year, and the following year a mother and two cubs took it over. On this later occasion a smaller bear, possibly an older cub of the denning mother, was asleep in another crack in the rocks only 10 feet away from the old female.

Despite the size of a mature black bear ready for a winter's sleep, it retires, sometimes, to amazingly small dens.

The World of the Black Bear

There seems to be little known of a black bear's inclination, or lack of inclination, to use the same den site year after year. However, my friends in Yellowstone National Park, Mr. and Mrs. L. C. Abbie, have described to me a couple of bears that returned to the same den site for several consecutive years.

One such bear was known as "Old Baxter." They described him as a "big friendly brown fellow, without a speck of bad habits." Old Baxter liked to sleep under the buildings at Mammoth and seemed to prefer the electrical shop. During the winter he had many visitors who would drop in to see and photograph him asleep. Mr. Abbie stated that Old Baxter's actions showed that these frequent visits, accompanied as they were by the light of flashbulbs and a certain amount of noise, were obviously disturbing. But the old bear seemed tolerant about it all and displayed no inclination to become mean at being disturbed so much.

The other hibernating bear described by the Abbies had located a den site a few feet above one of the area's hot springs. It slept there quite comfortably warmed by the heat from the spring for several winters. Unfortunately, the hot spring was also the bear's nemesis. Apparently it awoke sometime during the winter and, perhaps because it was groggy from sleep, fell into the hot spring and was killed.

There seems to be no evidence that a black bear normally feeds after embarking upon its winter's sleep. The fact that captive bears do feed more or less regularly during what would ordinarily be the period of winter sleep is probably meaningless, since these animals lead lives that vary a great deal from the wild. An examination of the inside and outside of a den containing a female bear disclosed no excretions during a period of ninety-eight days. This tends to indicate that during that period the bear's digestive system did not function.

Bears develop a fecal "plug" during their dormant period; its purpose is unclear. But this accumulation of residual material in the lower colon closes the alimentary tract. It has been suggested that the indiscriminate gleanings of which it is composed were consumed by

132

the bear after its period of active feeding for the specific purpose of forming the plug. This material, mixed with digestive secretions retained by the animal during this period, is normally ejected when the bear becomes active in the spring. Should a bear be sufficiently disturbed to flee from its den, it eliminates the "plug" instantly.

When black bears first retire to their dens in late November or December, they do not immediately drop off into the deep sleep which will carry them through most of the winter. For a week or more they exist in a half-awake, half-asleep condition, but eventually, as the weather grows colder, they become dormant. Like so many things about wild animals, however, this is not a hard and fast rule.

Richard Gerstell reports that some Pennsylvania black bears, apparently males, will remain active throughout mild and open winters. Warm spells occasionally bring black bears out of their dens in the northern states and Canada. They wander about for a while and then go back in again.

J. R. Matson's splendid record of observations of a female black bear and cubs in the den during the winter of 1951-52 has provided us with an excellent study of bear activity during the dormant period. We do not know, of course, how typical the actions of this bear were, but I would guess that other females with cubs behave in a somewhat similar fashion.

During the first period of observation, December 6 to January 4, tracks around the den showed that the female bear had made several trips in and out. Her cubs were born on January 3 or 4, and after that she remained in the den until March 13.

This bear was apparently in a very light sleep most of the time, for she seemed to become immediately aware of the approach of an observer. At no time did she show fear or animosity toward the intruders. Her most frequent reaction was merely to raise her head and look at them. I am inclined to think this might be attributed to a cautious approach to the den by the observers rather than to a normal black bear characteristic. On only one occasion, in early February, was it necessary for Mr. Matson to arouse the female by yelling at her.

The mother did considerable moving about within the den, and even after the cubs were born, she changed her position frequently. To keep the cubs warm she lay on her side with her hind legs well forward, and forelegs, head, and neck over the hind legs. Inside this enclosure the cubs were well protected. Mr. Matson reported that when she would raise her head the cubs could apparently feel the cold air and were quite noisy complaining about it.

By February 24 the cubs were crawling about inside the den and had been as far as the entrance, where their footprints could be seen in the snow. Shortly afterward the female enlarged the den, possibly because the growing cubs needed more room.

On March 23, the female and cubs were seen a short distance outside the den. The old bear had been feeding nearby, and the cubs were practicing tree climbing, although they apparently could only get up the trunk a couple of feet.

Not all bears are this tolerant of disturbances during the winter. Some have been known to move their cubs to other den locations and in one case, where the cubs had been handled with bare hands by a game warden, the female left them unattended in the old den for four days. Apparently, she would have nothing to do with them as long as they retained any human scent. Another female moved two cubs from a den site where she was disturbed to another den $2\frac{1}{4}$ miles away.

It seems likely that males, yearlings, and females without young cubs sleep more soundly than does a female with a pair of hungry 8-ounce newcomers. For example, Marius A. Morse describes a sleeping group of a female and three yearlings that did not react at all to ordinary conversation. Much shouting and whistling finally aroused the cubs, and they walked slowly away for some ten yards, apparently not frightened. The absence of the cubs seemed to arouse the female. She appeared quite groggy but got up and followed them. After a few minutes she was sufficiently awake to lead the cubs in a running retreat into denser cover.

Some bears are quick to resent a disturbance of their winter sleep. They may waken quickly and come charging out of their dens. In any event, bear dens should be approached with caution, and taking undue liberties with a dormant bear is always dangerous.

One of the truly amazing things about black bears is that after spending several months asleep in a winter den they come out looking as fat and as sleek as they did when they went in. There is apparently some weight loss, however, which has been estimated at 20 to 25 per cent. This presumably holds true with females who have had cubs during the winter. The largest weight loss occurs after they emerge in the spring and before there is sufficient food around to provide energy for the bear's active period. Fortunately, most individuals greet the spring with a reserve of fat that will see them through this time.

So far no way has been found to tell the exact age of a bear from its physical condition. The condition of the teeth is a criterion, but the best that can be told from teeth by observation alone is whether or not the bear is a young, mature, or old one. Recent studies involving a tooth sectioning technique show promise but the results are still inconclusive.

An age of twelve to fifteen years is generally accepted as a normal life span for a wild black bear. However, captive bears are known to have lived to twenty-seven years of age. A pair of captive bears produced young until they were twenty-one years old, a length of productivity of seventeen years. This might mean that, on the average, wild black bears are capable of reproducing during their entire adult lives.

Conclusion

THE BLACK BEAR is apparently a descendant of Asian ancestors that migrated onto this continent following the Pleistocene epoch, as it appears that those native to this country did not survive the ice age. They crossed over from Asia by way of the Bering Land Bridge into the unglaciated Yukon River Valley and then migrated south and east along the Rocky Mountain Trench and other intermountain valley systems. It also seems that at some later time black bear populations spread northward, probably with the gradual disappearance of the ice covering, to populate new territory, notably the islands in southeastern Alaska.

Prehistoric drawings of bears indicate that the animals have changed little since then. The drawings depict bears of much greater size than any of our present species, especially the black bear. But some of this may have been the result of artistic license on the part of these ancient artists.

It is certain, however, that bears of one kind or another have been with us for a long time, and the effect of their presence is indicated in many ways. The Bible mentions bears in Isaiah 59:11: "We roar like bears, and mourn like doves." Two of the best-known constellations, the Big Dipper and the Little Dipper, were given the names of Ursa Major, which means "Big Bear," and Ursa Minor, which means "Little Bear."

Bears have also been an influence in more recent times. Many of the place names in the United States reflect the importance placed on

136

bears in times past. Both Kentucky and Arkansas were nicknamed the "Bear State" because of the number of bears found there during the pioneer period. There are towns named *Bear* in Delaware, Arkansas, and Idaho. *Bear Creek* is even more favored and there are towns so named in Alabama, North Carolina, Pennsylvania, Wisconsin, and Wyoming. *Bear Lake* can be found in Michigan and Pennsylvania, and there is *Big Bear Lake* in California. Among other towns having a *Bear* name are Big Bear City, California; Bear Valley, California; Bear Branch, Kentucky; Bear Creek Springs, Arkansas; Bear Butte, South Dakota; and Bear River City, Utah. Utah also has a Bear River Bay in Great Salt Lake and a Bear River National Wildlife Refuge. In Colorado there is a 14,040-foot mountain named Little Bear Peak, and Montana has a lesser mountain named Bearpaw Mountain.

Real or fancied characteristics of the bear have also influenced some of our American slang and resulted in such expressions as "gruff as a bear," "bear hug," "hungry as a bear," and "He was a bear for punishment."

A term used in stock transactions—"a bear in the market"—applies to a stock purchaser who sells short (without owning the stock) and hopes for a lowering of prices. It comes from an old English proverb, "To sell the bearskin before one has caught the bear."

When the first white settlers established their precarious footholds on the Atlantic coast, black bears were present in large numbers in almost all of the wooded areas of the continent. They are still found in much of the same area, but a substantial reduction in size of suitable habitat has had its effect on populations. Any attempt at estimating the total number of black bears around in those early days is, of course, subject to many hazards. Seton suggested a primitive black bear population of at least 500,000. It could have been much greater. The vast timberlands of that period coupled with the bear's lack of enemies and its omnivorous diet could have produced a remarkably large bear population. A comparison of present-day population estimates and the

137

The World of the Black Bear

present-day black bear habitat with the probable extent of suitable black bear habitat during primitive periods supports the possibility of a much higher primitive bear population than Seton estimated.

An accurate inventory of present black bear population is, of course, impossible. However, the various states have estimated their bear populations from time to time and while these are admittedly only estimates, the figures provide some indication of numbers and whether or not they are increasing. All of the Canadian provinces list black bears in their present fauna but I was unable to obtain any estimates as to the numbers. Gilbert shows black bear populations in the United States as:

1937	81,270
1938	93,951
1943	151,653
1946	155,100
1947	131,900
1948	126,000

A 1957 leaflet published by the United States Department of the Interior, Fish and Wildlife Service, showed a compilation of population figures reported by the States (with the exception of Alaska) totaling 137,333. In November, 1964, the Alaskan Department of Fish and Game estimated a black bear population of 20,000.

According to the 1957 Fish and Wildlife Service report previously mentioned, states with bear populations in excess of 1,000 were:

California	22,000
Colorado	8,200
Idaho	8,000
Montana	6,570
New Mexico	1,500
Wyoming	2,000
Oregon	10,000
Minnesota	10,000
Washington	35,000

138

Maine	7,000
Michigan	5,000
New York	1,250
North Carolina	10,000
Pennsylvania	1,000
Vermont	2,000
Wisconsin	2,750

States reporting between 100 and 1,000 bears were:

Arizona	600
Utah	500
Alabama	200
Arkansas	100
Florida	450
Georgia	500
Louisiana	200
New Hampshire	800
South Carolina	250
Tennessee	250
Virginia	600
West Virginia	800

States reporting no bears or only token populations were:

Kansas	0
Nebraska	0
Nevada	0
North Dakota	0
Oklahoma	0
South Dakota	0
Texas	20
Connecticut	0
Delaware	0
Illinois	0
Indiana	0
Iowa	0
Kentucky	20
Maryland	0

Massachusetts	8
Mississippi	20
Missouri	12
New Jersey	12
Ohio	21
Rhode Island	0

Replies to queries made in 1964 to states with a large bear population were incomplete, but the information received, along with other published data, indicates that the number of black bears is increasing. Controlled hunting, better law enforcement, and facilities to prevent major forest fires appear to be responsible. Regulation of hunting, in particular, seems to affect the number of bears to be found in an area.

A fair estimate of the present black bear population in the United States (including Alaska) would be between 160,000 and 175,000 animals.

As the early settlers moved westward clearing the land of its covering of timber, building their cabins, and pasturing their livestock, their rifles made the first serious inroads on black bear populations. In addition to furnishing food, grease, and furs to the settlers, the black bear was thought to be a menace to livestock. Many were searched out and killed to protect domestic animals. Unlike the grizzly, whose disposition was not compatible with civilization, the black bear retreated in the face of this growing pressure farther into the wilderness and managed to survive, at least to some extent, in most of the areas where it was once so plentiful.

These wilderness pockets to which the black bear fled have, in some cases, become a part of our national park system. It is here that one has unequaled opportunity to observe black bears easily and safely. Yellowstone National Park and Great Smoky Mountains National Park are best known for this purpose, though I have spent many enjoyable hours "bear-watching" in Crater Lake National Park.

At times these park bears have caused considerable trouble but, in

140

Bear watching in our national parks is a popular pastime. The best way to observe is to disturb the bears as little as possible in order to see their natural actions rather than those influenced by the offer of food. One can do the latter in a zoo.

most cases, the trouble is the result of some action or lack of precaution on the part of unthinking, or uninformed, visitors to the area. A black bear has an insatiable appetite and more than its share of curiosity, both of which frequently get it into trouble. Garbage cans are fair game for the black bear and quickly become battered and worn as the animals work them over for the tidbits inside. Food left unprotected by campers attracts black bears as candy attracts kids, and often the results of leaving supplies untended are torn tents, ripped sleeping bags, and nothing left for the campers to eat.

141

The World of the Black Bear

Probably the worst bear trouble comes from visitors to the national parks who insist upon feeding the animals begging at the roadside despite repeated and constant warnings from the Park Service. These people come into the parks seemingly convinced that all its animals, and especially the bears, are pets. Nothing could be further from the truth. These are as wild as any bear one can find, but they have lost their fear of humans, and this may make them more dangerous.

I have met people who expressed grave concern about the danger from black bears while camping in the Cascade wilderness of central Oregon where bears run away at the first whiff of human scent. These same people will go to Yellowstone and hand-feed black bears in the false belief that they are perfectly safe. A black bear does not readily accept the idea that the supply of food coming from a visitor is exhausted, and when no more is offered it may reach up with a forepaw and give a not-so-gentle tap to suggest that the person is holding out; this tap may result in anything from a torn sleeve to a badly ripped arm. It almost inevitably results in irate complaints to the park rangers about the vicious bears.

It is unbelievable how foolish some people can be around park bears. I once saw a woman attempting to set her three-year-old daughter on the back of an old brown male so her husband could get a picture of such a memorable occasion. The timely arrival of a ranger put an end to an episode that might have resulted in tragedy.

On another occasion, a man was seen trying to push a bear into the driver's seat of his car beside his wife. He too wanted to get a memorable picture though it appeared that he may also have been trying to get rid of his wife. Often the photographer in a group will move some distance away in order to picture the bears standing up around his car and being fed by the occupants. Almost always he has a problem getting back, and more than once a photographer has found himself running in circles around his car trying to get far enough ahead of the pursuing bear to open the door and get in. The bear is not really after

Bears make very poor pets. They are always into trouble as cubs and always dangerous as adults.

the person but thinks there may be more food available and wants its share. Of course, females with cubs are always dangerous, and anyone molesting a cub is inviting a savage attack from the mother bear. In addition, the claws of a cub are quite sharp and will cut a person like tiny razors.

There is only one really safe and sane rule to follow with park bears: *Look at them and leave them alone.* This is best done from within one's car with the windows up. It is also actually better for the bears. If they become too aggressive toward people as a result of receiving constant handouts, they may eventually have to be destroyed as a safety precaution.

Black bears are on exhibit in nearly all zoos, and their popularity is attested to by the crowds feeding them peanuts, popcorn, and similar fare. They are most often kept in open pits, and they quickly learn the art of begging and performing for handouts from their audience. Most black bears seem to take readily to this form of captivity, especially in modern zoos where they have plenty of room.

Black bears make very poor pets, however. As cubs they are mischievous and troublesome. They cry incessantly when lonely or hungry, and because of their curiosity and climbing ability nothing is safe from their inquisitive noses and inquiring claws. I once watched a friend of mine who had a pair of cubs about six months old try to carry one that didn't want to be carried. The angry cub reached up with a tiny forepaw and raked him across the cheek, leaving a row of cuts that required medical attention.

Another friend, Mrs. Cliff Ralston of Redmond, Oregon, was given a yearling black bear that had been raised from a tiny cub. This one demonstrated more affection than I have seen before or since, but only toward Mrs. Ralston. It merely tolerated other people. It weighed about a hundred pounds, and Mrs. Ralston would take it for daily walks on a chain leash. The animal obviously enjoyed these excursions, especially the plunge in the river that terminated each one. Unfortu-

144

Mrs. Cliff Ralston of Redmond, Oregon, gives her yearling black bear its daily bath in a stream near her home.

nately, this bear, like so many wild pets, came to a sad end. It escaped from its pen one day and was accidentally killed while attempts were being made to recapture it.

I was told of an old male black bear that had been raised from a cub by a winter keeper at Tower Falls in Yellowstone National Park several years ago. It apparently grew up to be the bear counterpart of a "perfect gentleman" and was called "Pat." Once during Pat's younger days a park visitor who was hiking up a trail looked up to see a bear coming downhill on the same path. It was Pat, though the visitor didn't know it. Badly frightened, the man fell to his knees. Pat calmly leaped over him and went on down the hill. One of the park cooks would permit Pat to come into his kitchen and lie down near the stove. The cook's small daughter cruising about in her kiddie car would deliberately bump into the bear. Pat ignored the youngster or good naturedly moved when the bumps became too irritating.

Obviously old Pat was a most unusual bear. The general rule and the safest rule is to leave them all alone.

Adult black bears are much too large and strong to be trusted. They can be short tempered and this makes them unpredictable. It has been said that the most dangerous black bear is a pet one, and I am inclined to agree with this statement.

Despite the many opinions to the contrary, danger to man from black bear in the wilds is usually nonexistent. Most of the reports of black bear attacks, or ferocity, or danger, are the results of man's molesting a bear or the misinterpretation of bear actions. Hunters reporting on the actions of black bears wounded and surrounded by a pack of snarling hounds invariably emphasize the strength, savagery, and determination of the cornered animal. The dangers to themselves while facing this "deadly" beast are not minimized, to say the least, since one of the principle reasons for telling the story is to demonstrate their own bravery. However, almost any animal, no matter how small or normally timid, will fight back when cornered.

Conclusion

A black bear is a big strong animal, and when pressed it can be extremely dangerous. A black bear surrounded by dogs and hunters is mostly interested in getting away from its tormentors.

Quite often the mere sight of an unconfined black bear produces fear and trembling and eventually becomes the imagined story of a vicious bear attack. Recently, a game commission office in an eastern state that has a sizable black bear population received a frantic call from a mother. She reported that two bears had chased her sons up a tree. Upon advice of the game commission representative, the woman fired a couple of shots into the air and frightened the bears away. The true story, as later learned, was that the woman's sons had climbed an apple tree in order to shake down some fruit. A small black bear cub waddled into the orchard and under the tree and started eating apples. The boys were delighted with this turn of events and threw more apples to the cub. Finally, an old bear, the cub's mother, joined the cub for the free lunch. It was then that the boy's mother discovered the situation and decided that her sons had been attacked and treed by these bears.

Black bears do attack humans, however. Such incidents are rare and nearly always the result of provocation on the part of the person molested. Captive bears that were being continually annoyed and threatened accounted for many of the reported attacks. Wounded bears, females with cubs, and park bears cause all but a few of the balance.

Unprovoked attacks upon man by black bears are so rare as to warrant the statement that black bears are not dangerous. This is not to suggest, of course, that one should not exercise due caution in bear country or around bears for there is always some question as to just what might "provoke" a black bear. Just being too close might well result in an attack.

Among all of the documented unprovoked attacks on humans by black bears, and there aren't many, less than a half-dozen that I've been able to find, resulted in human deaths. These, for the most part,

147

apparently came from starving or extremely hungry bears. In one instance, described by Seton, a large black bear whose face and neck were stuck full of porcupine quills killed a trapper. In July and August of 1963, four assaults by black bears were made on persons in the Fairbanks area of Alaska. This was most unusual, both because of the unprecedented number and the fact that they were concentrated in the Fairbanks area. The reasons for these attacks were not discovered but an investigation seemed to rule out hunger, rabies, and population stress as logical explanations. The only significant fact seemed to be that, where identifications were made, the animals were males.

Not only have a black bear's dangerous aspects been overemphasized, but its predatory habits have been exaggerated. The occasional animal that develops a taste for livestock and is subsequently pursued relentlessly by hounds and hunters receives considerable attention, and the stories of the hunt grow more complex, more lurid, and more believable with each telling. The result is often an unjust condemnation of all black bears as killers of livestock.

A federal trapper examined thirty-five head of cattle believed to have been the victims of a killer bear and discovered they had died of larkspur poisoning. Scavenging bears had been blamed for their death. Many similar cases can be found where black bears have been blamed for livestock fatalities due to natural causes or other predators. It often happens that a dead animal is discovered by a black bear that, with its fondness for carrion, feeds on the carcass. Later the remains are discovered, and because there are bear tracks around, bears are blamed for the death.

It has been suggested that only one bear out of every hundred has a taste for meat and is a killer. Whether or not this ratio is reasonably accurate does not seem to me to be too important, since the meat eating tendencies of black bear appear to be influenced by the availability of other foods in an area. Thus it is possible that in certain territories the ratio could be considerably greater and in others much lower. In a wilderness where there are no livestock herds and black bear must rely upon deer, elk, or moose, the taste for meat may soon disappear in favor of the more readily available vegetable foods. The adults of these deer species are much too difficult for a bear to catch and kill to represent a reliable source of meat. A black bear may occasionally kill and eat a deer fawn or elk calf, but these appear to be individuals that it stumbled upon in its meanderings through the woods, rather than animals the bear purposefully searched out.

On the other hand, a bear in an area where there is much livestock may discover the ease with which sheep, goats, pigs, and cows can be killed. While this does not happen often, it appears that once a bear does turn to domestic animals for its food supply it does not readily go back to its more normal foods.

Investigations of cattle killed by black bears reveal that most of them died of a broken neck, apparently resulting from one or more powerful blows of the bear's forepaw. Sheep are also killed in this manner, although a bite through the neck or spine may be used. It is believed that when a bear is in the midst of a flock of sheep he strikes about with quick blows of the forepaw killing several rapidly. However, when a single sheep is attacked, the bite in the neck or spine may be used. Carcasses are usually dragged or carried to some concealed location nearby where the bear may feed at its leisure. As these kills generally represent more meat than a bear will eat at one time, the remains may be partly covered and the bear may return sometime later for another meal.

Stock-killing bears are almost always males, though on rare occasions stock-killing females have also been reported. These bears are usually either quite old or crippled. When a bear does become a stock killer, fences furnish little protection to domestic herds. In most cases animals in back pastures well away from any occupied dwellings will feel the brunt of an attack. The bear seems to prefer a concealed approach to the unsuspecting livestock, and will make use of wooded area or a

149

line of brush leading to the herd or to the edge of the field or orchard.

A scarcity of natural foods is probably the underlying cause of most of the damage bears do. They sometimes destroy whole apiaries and severely damage fruit trees in addition to preying on livestock. During their wanderings in search of food, bears occasionally come down into towns and create much excitement along with a great deal of unnecessary fright.

Black bears are held responsible for considerable injury to timber where the animals have either girdled the trunk or have severely damaged it. It appears that bears like the cambium layer of tissue and must, of course, remove the outer bark to get to it. In some states, Washington, for example, lumber companies consider this damage so extensive that they encourage bear hunting on their timber lands.

Careless campers and ill-constructed or poorly protected wilderness cabins often suffer from the attentions of hungry and ingenious black bear. Successful deer, elk, and moose hunters frequently find that a bear has helped himself to a quarter of meat hung unguarded in the woods to cool. Wooden forest direction signs are often destroyed by black bear to the consternation of woods travelers. In the Superior Forest country of Minnesota it is reported that black bears sometimes harm canoes left temporarily along the shores of wilderness waterways.

While it may seem that we have compiled a rather large list of black bear conflicts with man's interests, it should be remembered that only the occasional bear is a criminal, not the entire species, and that more often than not the "crime" may be inspired by human actions. The black bear also does some good as a result of its natural movements and food-seeking activities. Seeds get entangled in the thick hair and carried into other areas. In digging for ants, rodents, roots, and bulbs, black bears not only provide some control over the numbers of rodents, but help the planting and ultimate growth of natural seeds that may be lying about on top of the ground. Bears are great berry eaters and the seeds, passing through the digestive tract uninjured, may cause berry patches to be started in new locations. Their fondness for carrion has undoubtedly been of considerable benefit, since they consume the rotting remains of animals killed by accident or other means which might conceivably contaminate food or water supplies.

Like nearly every other species of wildlife, black bears have detractors who seem to desire their extinction or near extinction for any number of real or fancied reasons. They also have their supporters who find them not guilty of the majority of charges brought against the species, and the balance insignificant in the face of the animal's prominent position in the fauna of this country.

For a long time black bears were afforded little protection but gradually the states with bear populations have become aware of the need for it. Almost all states have established some means of shielding the species. Restricted hunting of adults and closed seasons on cubs seem to be the most desirable of the controls currently in force. Since the black bear has practically no effective enemies other than man and is not susceptible to winter starvation and summer food failures, hunting seems to be the most workable and controllable means of regulating bear populations.

I think that there can be little fear of an unrestricted growth in numbers of black bear; such growth would result in a head-on collision with civilization and ultimate disastrous effects on black bears. At the same time there is little reason for not letting the black bear population increase to the maximum supportable by the available black bear habitat.

I think we shall continue to hear of adventures of black bears from hunters, campers, and careless park visitors. But these merely add spice to life and a feeling of adventure to wilderness outings.

Black Bear Subspecies

Bears evolved from a family of small tree-climbing carnivorous mammals, called the Miacidae, that lived some fifty million years ago. From a subfamily, the Miacinae, came the Procyonidae (raccoons, coatis), Canidae (coyotes, wolves, and dogs), and the Ursidae (black bear, grizzly bear, and big brown bear). They are classified as phylum Chordata because they have backbones and as mammals because they are warm-blooded, have four-chambered hearts, body hair, give birth to their young alive, and have mammary glands with which to nurse their young. As flesh eaters, they are in the order Carnivora though they have developed into omnivorous creatures.

Black bears belong in the family Ursidae of the genus *Ursus*. Species of this genus on the North American continent include *Ursus americanus*, the black bear; *Ursus horribilis*, the grizzly bear; and *Ursus middendorffi*, the big brown (Kodiak) bear.

The following list of races and subspecies of the black bear follows the systematic names of E. Raymond Hall and Keith R. Kelson in their *The Mammals of North America*. The approximate ranges represent the areas generally indicated by most authorities. However, the black bear is a woods animal and would only be found in the timbered sections of such ranges.

Ursus americanus americanus. American black bear. Range: Canada except western portions, eastern and central United States except parts of Florida, Alabama, Mississippi, and Louisiana.

152

Black Bear Subspecies

Ursus americanus altifrontalis. Olympic black bear. Range: Southern British Columbia (except Vancouver Island), central and western Washington, central and western Oregon, northwestern California.

Ursus americanus amblyceps. New Mexico black bear. Range: Southeastern Utah, Colorado except northeast and east, north, southeast and south central New Mexico, extreme eastern Texas, Chihuahua and Durango in Mexico, and eastern Arizona.

Ursus americanus californiensis. California black bear. Range: North and eastern California except in south.

Ursus americanus cinnamomum. Cinnamon bear. Range: Western Montana, western Wyoming, northeastern Utah, Idaho, western Oregon, western Washington, extreme southeastern British Columbia and extreme southwestern Alberta.

Ursus americanus eremicus. East Mexico bear. Northeastern Mexico.

Ursus americanus floridanus. Florida black bear. Range: Florida.

Ursus americanus luteolus. Louisiana black bear. Range: Louisiana and Mississippi along Mississippi River.

Ursus americanus carlottae. Queen Charlotte black bear. Range: Queen Charlotte Islands in west British Columbia.

Ursus americanus emmonsii. Glacier bear. Range: Southeastern Alaska.

Ursus americanus hamiltoni. Newfoundland black bear. Range: Newfoundland.

Ursus americanus hunteri. Mackenzie black bear. Range: Southeastern Yukon territory.

Ursus americanus kermodei. Kermode black bear. Range: West central British Columbia.

Ursus americanus machetes. West Mexico black bear. Range: Chihuahua, Mexico.

Ursus americanus perniger. Kenai black bear. Range: Kenai Peninsula, Alaska.

153

The World of the Black Bear

Ursus americanus pugnax. Dall black bear. Range: Dall Island, Alaska.

Ursus americanus randi. Yukon black bear. Range: central Yukon territory.

Ursus americanus vancouveri. Vancouver black bear. Range: Vancouver Island, British Columbia.

Bibliography

Albright, Horace M., "Why Bears Behave Like Human Beings." *Collier's*, Vol. 83, No. 26 (June 29, 1929), pp. 26, 28, 36.

Aldous, Shaler E., "A Hibernating Black Bear with Cubs." *Journal of Mammalogy*, 18:466 (1937).

Bennett, Logan J., English, P. F., and Watts, R. L., "The Food Habits of the Black Bear in Pennsylvania." *Journal of Mammalogy*, 24:25 (1943).

Black, Hugh C., "Black Bear Research in New York." *Transactions of the Twenty-third North American Wildlife Conference*, pp. 443-461. Washington, Wildlife Management Institute, 1958.

Black, J. D., "Mammals of Northwestern Arkansas." *Journal of Mammalogy*, 17:29 (1936).

Blair, Neal L., "Bears—Fact and Fancy." *Wyoming Wildlife*, Vol. 26, No. 4 (April, 1962), pp. 28-31.

Boyer, Richard L., "Mountain Coyotes Kill Yearling Black Bear in Sequoia National Park." *Journal of Mammalogy*, 30:75 (1949).

Burns, Eugene, *The Sex Life of Wild Animals*. New York, Rinehart & Company, Inc., 1953.

Burroughs, Raymond Darwin, editor, *The Natural History of the Lewis & Clark Expedition*. East Lansing, Michigan State University Press, 1961.

Burt, William H., *The Mammals of Michigan*. Ann Arbor, The University of Michigan Press, 1946.

Cahalane, Victor H., "Don't Feed the Bears." *The Saturday Evening Post*, Vol. 211, No. 4 (July 23, 1938), pp. 23, 62, 63, 65.

Cahalane, Victor H., *Mammals of North America*. New York, The Macmillan Company, 1947.

Cahn, Alvin R., "The Mammals of Itasca County, Minnesota." *Journal of Mammalogy*, 2:68 (1921).

Cameron, Austin W., "A New Black Bear from Newfoundland." *Journal of Mammalogy*, 37:538 (1956).

Carhart, Arthur H., *The Outdoorsman's Cookbook*. New York, The Macmillan Company, 1944.

Carrington, Richard, *The Mammals*. New York, Time Incorporated, 1963.

Chapman, Wendell, "Bears Will Be Boys." *Nature Magazine*, Vol. 24, No. 3 (September, 1934), pp. 103-107.

Coggswell, John F., "Too Many Bears!" *Saturday Evening Post*, Vol. 213, No. 40 (April 5, 1941), pp. 27, 94-97.

Cottam, Clarence, Nelson, A. L., and Clarke, Talbott E., "Notes on Early Winter Food Habits of the Black Bear in George Washington National Forest." *Journal of Mammalogy*, 20:310 (1939).

Crandall, Lee S., *The Management of Wild Mammals in Captivity*. Chicago, The University of Chicago Press, 1964.

Cunningham, Bill, "Boss of the Bush." *Collier's*, Vol. 104, No. 20 (November 11, 1939), pp. 22, 67, 68.

Dailey, E. J., *Traplines and Trails*. Columbus, The Hunter-Trader-Trapper Co., 1925.

Davis, David E., and Golley, Frank B., *Principles in Mammalogy*. London, Chapman and Hall, Ltd., 1963.

Davis, Hugh, "Life with Bongo." *Nature Magazine*, Vol. 42, No. 1 (January, 1949), pp. 25-27.

Devoe, Alan, *This Fascinating Animal World*. New York, McGraw-Hill Book Company, Inc., 1951.

Drahos, Nick, "Biggest Bear in the East." *Outdoor Life*, Vol. 131, No. 5 (May, 1963), pp. 52-55, 136, 137, 139, 140, 141.

East, Ben, "Biggest Black Ever Killed." *Outdoor Life*, Vol. 133, No. 5 (May, 1964), pp. 46-48, 127-131.

Erickson, Albert W., "Techniques for Live-Trapping and Handling Black Bears." *Transactions of the Twenty-second North American Wildlife Conference*, pp. 520-543. Washington, Wildlife Management Institute, 1957

Erickson, Albert W., "The Age of Self-Sufficiency in the Black Bear." *Journal of Wildlife Management*, 23:401 (1959).

Erickson, Albert W., "Supernumerary mammae in the Black Bear." *Journal of Mammalogy*, 41:409 (1960).

Bibliography

Erickson, Albert W., and Martin, Paul, "Black Bear Carries Cubs from Den." *Journal of Mammalogy*, 41:408 (1960).

Erickson, Albert W., Nellor, John, and Petrides, George A., *The Black Bear in Michigan*. East Lansing, Michigan State University, 1964.

Fournier, Paul J., "Can Animals Talk?" *Field & Stream*, Vol. 69, No. 2 (June, 1964), pp. 52-54, 143, 150.

Gerstell, Richard, "The Growth and Size of Pennsylvania Black Bears." *Pennsylvania Game News*, Vol. 10, No. 8 (November, 1939), p. 4.

Gilbert, Douglas L., "Economics and Related Biology of the Black Bear in Colorado." Unpublished M. S. Thesis, Colorado A. & M. College, 1951.

Glover, Fred A., "Black Bear Damage to Redwood Reproduction." *Journal of Wildlife Management*, 19:437 (1955).

Golley, Frank, *Mammals of Georgia*. Athens, University of Georgia Press, 1962.

Grinnell, Joseph, Dixon, Joseph, and Linsdale, Jean M., *Fur Bearing Mammals of California*. Berkeley, University of California Press, 1937.

Grove, Alvin R., Jr., "Bear Facts." *Pennsylvania Game News*, Vol. 28, No. 11 (November, 1957), pp. 7-13.

Hall, E. Raymond, *Mammals of Nevada*. Berkeley, University of California Press, 1946.

Hall, E. Raymond and Kelson, Keith R., *The Mammals of North America*. New York, The Ronald Press, 1959.

Hamilton, W. J., Jr., *American Mammals*. New York, McGraw-Hill Book Company, Inc., 1939.

Hamilton, William J., Jr., *The Mammals of Eastern United States*. Ithaca, Comstock Publishing Co., 1943.

Harlow, Richard F., "Characteristics and Status of Florida Black Bear." *Transactions of the Twenty-Sixth North American Wildlife and Natural Resources Conference*, pp. 481-495. Washington, Wildlife Management Institute, 1961.

Harrison, George H., "The Keystone Bruin." *Pennsylvania Game News*, Vol. 35, No. 1 (January, 1964), pp. 7-13.

Herring, Joe L., "Black Bear in Louisiana." *Louisiana Conservationist*, Vol. 14, No. 1 (January, 1962), pp. 10-11.

Hill, John Eric, "Notes on Mammals of Northeastern New Mexico." *Journal of Mammalogy*, 23:75 (1942).

Howard, William Johnston, "Notes on the Hibernation of a Captive Black Bear." *Journal of Mammalogy*, 16:321 (1935).

Howell, A. Brazier, "The Black Bear as a Destroyer of Game." *Journal of Mammalogy*, 2:36 (1921).

Jackson, Hartley H. T., "A Record Black Bear." *Journal of Mammalogy*, 20:252 (1939).

Kephart, Horace, *Camp Cookery*. New York, The Macmillan Company, 1944.

Kephart, Horace, *Camping and Woodcraft*. New York, The Macmillan Company, 1964.

Kinney, Paul B., "The Ways of a Bear." *Nature Magazine*, Vol. 33, No. 10 (December, 1940), pp. 573-576.

Kinney, Paul B., "Once in a Lifetime." *The National Geographic Magazine*, Vol. 80, No. 2 (August, 1941), pp. 249-258.

Leach, Maria, Editor, *Standard Dictionary of Folklore, Mythology, and Legend*. New York, Funk & Wagnalls Company, 1949.

Leopold, A. Starker, *Wildlife of Mexico*. Berkeley, University of California Press, 1959.

Lindau, Bill, "Bare Facts About Bears." *Wildlife in North Carolina*, Vol. 16, No. 12 (December, 1952) pp. 8, 9, 20.

Luttringer, Leo A., Jr., "The Truth About the Black Bear." *Nature Magazine*, Vol. 25, No. 6 (June, 1935). pp. 323-325.

Martin, George W., *Come and Get It!* New York, A. S. Barnes and Company, 1942.

Matson, J. R., "Notes on Dormancy in the Black Bear." *Journal of Mammalogy*, 27:203 (1946).

Matson, J. R., "Litter Size in the Black Bear." *Journal of Mammalogy*, 33:246 (1952).

Matson, J. R., "Observations on the Dormant Phase of a Female Black Bear." *Journal of Mammalogy*, 35:28 (1954).

Matthew, W. D., "The Phylogeny of Dogs." *Journal of Mammalogy*, 11:117 (1930).

Miller, Loye, "Color Change in the Black Bear, *Ursus Americanus*." *Journal of Mammalogy*, 36:460 (1955).

Miller, Richard S., "Weights and Color Phases of Black Bear Cubs." *Journal of Mammalogy*, 44:129 (1963).

Moore, Clifford B., *Ways of Mammals*. New York, The Ronald Press Company, 1953.

Bibliography

Morse, Marius A., "Hibernation and Breeding of the Black Bear." *Journal of Mammalogy*, 18:460 (1937).

Murie, Adolph, "Some Food Habits of the Black Bear." *Journal of Mammalogy*, 18:238 (1937).

McCracken, Harold, *The Beast That Walks Like a Man*. Garden City, Hanover House, 1955.

McCracken, Harold, and Van Cleve, Harry, *Trapping*. New York, A. S. Barnes & Company, 1947.

Niehuis, Dave, "Art of Varmint Calling." *Outdoor Life*, Vol. 136, No. 2 (August, 1965), pp. 36-39, 74-75.

Norris-Elye, L. T. S., "The Black Bear as a Predator of Man." *Journal of Mammalogy*, 32:222 (1951).

O'Conner, Jack and Goodwin, Geo. G., *The Big Game Animals of North America*. New York, E. P. Dutton & Co., Inc., 1961.

Orr, Robert T., *Mammals of Lake Tahoe*. San Francisco, California Academy of Sciences, 1949.

Palmer, Ralph S., *The Mammal Guide*. Garden City, Doubleday & Company, Inc., 1954.

Popham, Arthur C., Jr., "Rare White Black-bear." *Outdoor Life*, Vol. 127, No. 4 (April, 1961), pp. 52-55, 139-143.

Richards, E. V., "Virginia's Black Bear—Good or Bad?" *Virginia Wildlife*, Vol. 14, No. 2 (February, 1953), pp. 16-17, 21, 23.

Richards, Elmer V., "Some Bear Facts." *Virginia Wildlife*, Vol. 18, No. 3 (March, 1957), pp. 8-9.

Rush, W. M., "How Fast Does a Black Bear Climb?" *Journal of Mammalogy*, 9:335 (1928).

Rush, W. M., "Diphyllobothrium Latum in Bear." *Journal of Mammalogy*, 13:274 (1932).

Rust, Henry Judson, "Mammals of Northern Idaho." *Journal of Mammalogy*. 27:308 (1946).

Schoonmaker, "Notes on the Black Bear in New York State." *Journal of Mammalogy*, 19:501 (1938).

Schwartz, Charles W. and Elizabeth R., *The Wild Mammals of Missouri*. Columbia, University of Missouri Press. 1959.

Seton, Ernest Thompson, *Lives of Game Animals*. Boston, Charles T. Branford Company, 1909.

Silver, Helenette, *A History of New Hampshire Game and Furbearers*. Concord, New Hampshire Fish and Game Department, 1957.

159

Skinner, M. P., *Bears in the Yellowstone*. Chicago, A. C. McClurg & Co., 1925.

Smith, Bertrand E., "Bear Facts." *Journal of Mammalogy*, 27:31 (1946).

Smith, Fred G., "A Warden's View." *Outdoor Life*. Vol. 135, No. 6 (June, 1965), pp. 56-57, 126-129, 143.

Soper, J. Dewey, "Mammals of Wood Buffalo Park, Northern Alberta and District of Mackenzie." *Journal of Mammalogy*, 23:119 (1942).

Spencer, Howard E., Jr., *The Black Bear and its Status in Maine*. Augusta, State of Maine Department of Inland Fisheries and Game, 1961.

Strobel, Ed., "Biggest Black Bear Ever." *Outdoor Life*, Vol. 121, No. 4 (April, 1958), pp. 70-71, 106, 110.

Surber, Thadeus, *The Mammals of Minnesota*. Saint Paul, Minnesota Game and Fish Department, 1932.

Wade, Otis, "The Behavior of Certain Spermophiles with Special Reference to Aestivation and Hibernation." *Journal of Mammalogy*, 11:160 (1930).

Warren, Edward Royal, *The Mammals of Colorado*. Norman, University of Oklahoma Press, 1942.

Welch, Dorothy, "Bears in Estes Park, Colorado." *Journal of Mammalogy*, 15:242 (1934).

Whittlack, S. C. "The Black Bear as a Predator of Man." *Journal of Mammalogy*, 31:135 (1950).

Wilson, Eddie W., "The Bear in Early America." *Virginia Wildlife*, Vol. 20, No. 1 (January, 1959), pp. 20-21.

Wilwerding, Walter J., "Bears of the World." *Sports Afield*, Vol. 142, No. 4 (October, 1959), p. 49.

Wright, William H., *The Black Bear*. New York, Charles Scribner's Sons, 1910.

Yeager, Dorr C., "Bringing Up Barney." *Nature Magazine*, Vol. 21, No. 1 (January, 1933), pp. 27-30.

Young, J. Z., *The Life of Mammals*. New York, Oxford University Press, 1957.

Index

Abbie, L. C., 40-41, 132
Adaptation to environment, 89
Albinos, 103
Anatomic differences, from grizzly bear, 24
Ancestry, 136
Appearance, 15
Aster root ("bear root," "bear medicine"), 44
Astronomy, constellations, 136
Attack by bear, defense by man, 47
Autumn activities, 102-123

"Bear tree," 111-113
Beds, 90-91
Berries in diet, 75, 76, 78, 150-151
Best, Alan, 20
Bible references, 137
Big brown bear, 11
    as enemy, 93
Bluffing, 61-62

Cahalane, Victor H., 50
Cannibalism, 80
Captivity, potential danger, 27
Cascade Mountains, Oregon, 107
Characteristics of bears, real or fancied, 137
Classification of bears, 152-154
Claws, 107, 109-110
Color, 103-104
    phase, 17, 20-21
    unreliable in identification, 16-17
    variations, 17, 20-21
Crater Lake National Park, 20, 35, 36, 41, 62-63, 140
Cubs, abandonment by mother in danger, 73-74

appearance, several weeks old, 55
attainment of self-sufficiency, 82
birth, 133-134
    months, 50
climbing trees, teaching by mother, 71, 73
crawling and walking, 55-56
discipline by mother, 74
emergence from hibernation, weight, 113-115
food, search for, 59
fur, 115
    development, 55
in hibernation, care by mother, 55
indulgence by mother, 74
man as greatest enemy, 73
newborn, number in litter, 51, 52
    sex ratio, 52
    size, 51
nursing, 53-55
play, 74-75
rearing, as entire responsibility of mother, 70
restricting on killing, 120
weaning, 101
yearlings, 83

Danger to man in wilds, 146-148, 150
Den, 127-132
Diet, 75-76, 78, 80, 81
    preferred foods, 80-81
    variations determined by local resources, 75
Diseases, 92
Drawings, prehistoric, 136

Enemies, 93-94
Evolution of bear families, 152

161

The World of the Black Bear

Fat, bear, importance to Indians and pioneers, 38-39
Feet, 107, 109-111
Female, fertility, length of period, 87
  offspring, number during life span, 87
Fighting, 62, 64, 70
  by males during mating period, 86-87
Forest fires as menace, 85-86
Fruit in diet, 78
Fur, characteristics, 57, 59
  of cubs, 115
  as headgear in Canada and England, 121
  shedding in spring, 56-57, 59

Gait, 104-107
Garbage can, bearproof, 27
Gerstell, Richard, 133
Gestation, "delayed implantation" of ovum, 50-51
  length of period, 50
Gilbert, Douglas L., 138
Great Smoky Mountains National Park, 140
Grease of bear, as cooking oil, 122-123
Grinnell, Joseph, 20, 130
Grizzly bear(s), 11
  anatomic differences from black bear, 24
  climbing trees, 32
  color variations, 24
  as enemy, 93
Growth, period of, 21-22

Habitat and range, 11, 29-32
  in pioneer days, 137-138
  size of territory, 88-89
Hall, E. Raymond, and Keith R. Kelson, The Mammals of North America, races and subspecies of black bears, 152-154
Health, 91-93
Hibernation, appearance at end of, 135
  in captivity, 126
  vs. "deep sleep," 124-127
  den, 127-132
  development of fecal "plug" in dormant period, 132-133
  disturbance of, 135
  emergence from den, 48-50
  erroneous beliefs, 45
  feeding before, 125-127
  length of period, 126

  mystery of, 45
  purpose of, 125-127
Honey in diet, 75, 76, 78
Hornaday, William T., 20, 21
Hunters of bears, adventure stories, 38, 146
  guns used, 119
  hound packs, 117-118
  number of black bears killed annually, 120
  restrictions on killing black bears, 151
  seasons, open and closed, 119-120

Indians, bears in legends, dances and ceremonies, 42, 44, 45, 47
  Chiricahua Apache, 44
  Osage, 44
  Pueblo, 44
Insects in diet, 75, 76
Intelligence, 25, 27

Kephart, Horace, 123
Kermode subspecies, 20
Killers of stock, 148-150

"Lava Bears," 21
Legends about bears, 42, 44, 45, 47
Lewis and Clark Expedition, 89
Life span, 135

Male(s), courting, 86
  fighting during mating period, 86-87
  sexual maturity, age, 85
Mammals of North America, by E. Raymond Hall and Keith R. Kelson, races and subspecies of black bears, 152-154
Mating, 83-87
  courting, 86
  fighting among males, 86-87
  first time, age, 85
  frequency, 85
  monogamy on year-to-year basis, 86
  months, 50
Matson, J. R., 53, 97, 133
  quoted, 127
Meat, bear, human consumption, 121-122
  importance to Indians and pioneers, 38-39
  in diet of black bear, 75, 78, 80
  killers of stock, 148-150
Miacidae, black bear evolved from, 11
Migration, 136

162

Index

Misinformation about bears, 11
Monogamy on year-to-year basis, 86
Morse, Marius A., 126, 134

Number of black bears, 15
Nuts and seeds in diet, 78

Pain, behavior of bear, 99
Palmer, Ralph S., 123, 125
Parasites, 92
Pet bears, 27, 144, 146
Place names in United States, 136-137
Polar bear, 11
Popham, Arthur C., Jr., 20
Population, black bears, United States, by
    states and years, 138-140
Porcupines, 94
Predatory habits, exaggeration of, 148

Races and subspecies of black bears, 152-
    154
Ralston, Mrs. Cliff, 144
Range, governed by food supply, 91
Records of North American Big Game,
    compiled by Boone and Crockett Club
    (1964), 22
Refuse pits, behavior of bears at, 37-38
    in national parks, as source of food,
    60-61
Reputation, undeservedly bad, 117
Richards, E. V., 118
Running, speed, 104-106

Search for food, 40-42
Sequoia National Park, 55
Seton, Ernest Thompson, 103, 137, 138,
    148
Shoshone National Forest, Wyoming, 103
Shyness, 25
Size, variations, 22, 24
Skinner, M. P., 95, 115
    quoted, 55
Skins, bear, importance to Indians and
    pioneers, 38-39
    commercial value, 121
Skull, measurements, 22
Smith, Bertrand E., quoted, 55-56
Spring activities, 48-81
Standing on hind legs, 32
Strength, 24-25
Summer activities, 82-101

Switzenberg, D. F., 130
Symbolism attached to bears by Indians,
    44

Teeth, 87-88
    first permanent, 114
    injuries and infection, 93
Terms used in stock transactions, 137
Timber, injury by black bears, 150
Trails as highways, 90
Traps, steel, 120, 121
    bait, 120
    bear as easy prey to, 27
Trees, climbing, as defense, 32, 35
    speed, 35
    teaching by mother, 71
    use of hind legs, 32
    descent from, 35

United States Department of the Inte-
    rior, Fish and Wildlife Service, 120
    population figures for black bears,
    138-140
Ursidae, members of family, 11

Vegetables in diet, 75, 81
Virginia Wildlife, by Eddie W. Wilson,
    quoted, 122
Vision, 38
Visitors to national parks, trouble with
    bears, 140-142, 144
Vocal abilities, 97-99

Walla Walla River, South Fork, Oregon,
    104
Water, bathing, swimming and fishing,
    99-100
Weight, at emergence from hibernation,
    113-115
    variations, 22, 24
Wilson, Eddie W., *Virginia Wildlife,*
    quoted, 122
Winter, 124-135
Wright, William H., 17, 97, 125

Yellowstone National Park, 20, 25, 27, 40,
    61, 85, 95, 97, 132, 140, 142, 146
Yosemite National Park, 90

Zoos, black bears in, 144

163